The Microbe's Contribution to Biology

A. J. KLUYVER

and

C. B. VAN NIEL

Harvard University Press

Cambridge, Massachusetts

1956

DISTRIBUTED IN GREAT BRITAIN BY
GEOFFREY CUMBERLEGE, OXFORD UNIVERSITY PRESS, LONDON

LIBRARY OF CONGRESS CATALOG CARD NUMBER 56–5343
PRINTED IN THE UNITED STATES OF AMERICA

Preface

This printed version of the "John M. Prather Lectures," delivered by the two authors at Harvard University in April 1954, is an unpretentious book. It is not meant for microbiologists, who must inevitably realize that it does not contain a harmonious summary of present-day microbiological knowledge. The lecturers were given to understand that their audience would be composed of staff members and students specializing in many divergent phases of biological science. Hence it seemed appropriate to devote the lectures to a brief survey of some aspects of microbiological research which, in the opinion of the authors, have contributed significant principles to an interpretation of the behavior of living organisms. We hope that this approach may appeal sufficiently to biologists in general to justify the present publication.

It should be evident that the time element imposed drastic limitations on the amount of material that could be treated. This has resulted in the neglect of some important fields of microbiological research, such as virology. Furthermore, the nature of the lectures implied that the authors had to draw freely on the work of many microbiologists; it is to be hoped that we have done justice to their notable contributions.

Although the printed version adheres closely to the text of the lectures as delivered, it was considered desirable to expand the documentation for some of the conclusions and to delete certain passages of a more digressive nature.

The references should not be considered as an adequate bibliography of the subject matter. They are mainly intended to guide the nonmicrobiologist to some of the classical papers and general reviews pertaining to the major topics. It seemed, however, desirable to include in addition a number of publications on which the salient points of the discussions are based. This accounts for the decidedly heterogeneous character of the lists.

On several occasions the authors have pondered the question of why the task of delivering these lectures was assigned to them. We have concluded that this should be attributed to the fact that for more than three decades we have followed developments in microbiology with keen interest. During the first six years of this period this was possible under conditions of close and almost daily personal contact; subsequently a spatial separation of some 6,000 miles made necessary individual effort, aided by correspondence and rare encounters. For us one of the great attractions of the Prather Lectures will always remain the opportunity thus provided to resume our personal contact after a lapse of nearly eighteen years.

We wish to acknowledge our profound indebtedness to the Committee on the Prather Lectures of Harvard University which issued the invitation, in particular to Dr. Kenneth V. Thimann, who has spared no effort to effectuate the project for which he took the initiative as early as 1951. The warm reception he prepared for us, and the many pleasant and stimulating discussions with him, will be gratefully remembered.

The hospitality proffered by the President and Fellows of Harvard University and by the staff of the Biological Laboratories is also deeply appreciated.

In addition, the authors wish to thank all those who have contributed to making this publication posssible, especially the scientists, editors, and publishers who have kindly permitted the reproduction of figures; the sources of these are acknowledged in the legends.

A. J. K.
C. B. v. N.

Delft, Netherlands
Pacific Grove, California
November 1954–February 1955.

Contents

The Microbe's Contribution to Biology

1

Microbial metabolism and the energetic basis of life

A. J. KLUYVER

Less than three full centuries have passed since microbes were discovered. Until that time mankind lived in blissful ignorance of the essential role which microbes play in the subsistence of the human race on earth. And it even took another 150 years after the discovery of the first microbe before this insight began to dawn, thanks to the penetrating studies of men like Ehrenberg and Pasteur. Nowadays most scientists are vaguely aware that something would go wrong if somebody were to succeed in exterminating the microbe world. Few people, however, realize how quickly terrestrial surroundings would deteriorate, transforming our greenest pastures and our tropical forests into barren areas. Further disconsolate horrors of life on a microbeless earth are excellently described by Rahn in his *Microbes of merit*.[1]

Without entering into details, we may, therefore, take as a starting point the recognition that all of us are personally indebted to the microbe without which only a few human individuals, by taking very special measures, would be able to lead a highly artificial and charmless life.

The purpose of these lectures is to consider the question in what respects the biologist's outlook would be different if he had continued to ignore—consciously or unconsciously—all forms of life invisible to the naked eye. I believe that such an attitude would inevitably have led to a serious underevaluation of life's potencies, and this volume is an attempt to document this statement.

Let us first of all try to imagine what would happen to a biologist who has restricted his attention exclusively to the higher forms of life, and is then suddenly confronted with microbes.

Now some will probably object that it is senseless to discuss such a hypothetical case, and observe that microbiology has developed very smoothly in the hundred years of its existence, so that its results have quite gradually become available to the biologist. To this I reply that since Pasteur's startling discoveries of the important role played by microbes in human affairs, microbiology as a science has always suffered from its eminent practical implications. By far the majority of the microbiological studies were undertaken to answer questions either directly or indirectly connected with the well-being of mankind. In the first half of the 19th century only a few scientists with a wider interest had made more or less incidental excursions into the microbe world, and the trophies brought home from these expeditions had only very incompletely been incorporated into the general biological picture.

Toward the beginning of the present century the situation began to change. Under the influence of the magnificent examples set by a few pioneers like Cohn, Winogradsky, and Beijerinck, the number of disinterested workers in the microbiological field increased steadily. Gradually so many data regarding the occurrence and behavior of microorganisms had accumulated that biologists began to realize that they could no longer continue to ignore microbial manifestations.

To a certain extent it is therefore justified to say that the biologist of the 20th century has been more or less suddenly confronted with the microbe world. And I think I may add that the digestion of all these findings has proved to be a slow process which even today is still far from finished. On the other hand, it is clear that the increased interest in the microbe also led to a gradual penetration of general biological principles into microbiology.

Now it seems to me that the student of only the higher forms of life, on becoming acquainted with the microbe world, would experience a first shock when he learns that vast parts of the earth's crust—which he always had considered to be devoid, or almost devoid, of life—are in reality teeming with invisible living organisms. This holds equally well for seemingly barren patches of surface soil and for deeper soil layers, surface and subsurface waters, and even the atmosphere. Our "macrobiologist"—as we may perhaps call him for the sake of simplicity—would probably be inclined to find some consolation in the idea that these tiny unicellular organisms can be considered as mere curiosities of minor importance for life's terrestrial activities. But this illusion would not last long either, for the microbiologist would draw his attention to the following facts.

Reliable estimates have shown that the amount of carbon dioxide consumed annually in the photosynthetic activity of the green plants is such that the quantity of this gas present in the atmosphere would be exhausted within some 30 years, if it were not replenished. Even taking into account the important carbon dioxide reservoir present in the oceans as a buffer system, such an exhaustion should have occurred within historic times. It is, therefore, clear that the green plants can continue to grow only because the assimilated carbon is in some way reconverted into carbon dioxide. At first sight this will not present any difficulties to our "macrobiologist"; he will refer to the slow combustion of the vegetable remains by man and animals. However, several independent estimates tend to show that the annual carbon dioxide production by this means amounts to only about 5 percent of the annual carbon dioxide consumption by the green plants. The conclusion seems inevitable that the remaining 95 percent is produced by the mineralizing action of the microbe. As far as is known, Louis Pasteur [2] and Ferdinand Cohn [3] were the first to realize the indispensability of decay for the maintenance of life on earth, and to state explicitly that microbes are the driving force in this process. The corollary of this conclusion is that the total weight of microbial protoplasm on earth exceeds that of animal protoplasm by many times. Ignoring the microbe would obviously mean that a very considerable part—perhaps almost one-half—of the living protoplasm on earth is left out of consideration.

We shall see, however, that this quantitative aspect is certainly not the main reason why the biologist cannot afford to live on in ignorance of the microbe.

It seems likely that a "macrobiologist" who entered the micro-biological scene around 1910 would have been most impressed by the great diversity in properties of the microbial species to which he was introduced by the microbiologist. On inquiring into the natural habitats of all these different types of microbes he would get rather definite answers only for a certain number of special-ized types, such as animal and plant parasites, or organisms living in environments where very specific conditions more or less con-stantly prevail, as in hot springs or salt lakes. Microscopic ex-amination of such habitats often reveals the presence of readily identifiable microbes. But if he asks from what special materials the microbiologist had isolated the majority of his cultures, he would probably be referred to some arbitrary sample of soil, mud, or water, or even to the atmosphere. This answer would be all the more baffling to our "macrobiologist" because direct microscopic examination of such materials would fail to show anything like the large variety of microbes that can be isolated from them.

Then the microbiologist would come to his aid, and give him the following explanation. Experience has shown that a very large number of microbes may be considered to be almost ubiqui-tous. This does not mean that they are everywhere in considerable numbers, but that a few individuals of the species succeed in maintaining themselves at very divergent spots on earth, either in a dormant state or by temporary and localized outbursts fol-lowed by a slow decline of the micropopulation formed. More-over, many of these germs are of the airborne type, and localities temporarily devoid of a certain microbe may soon be repopulated from places where the germ in question has just flourished. Tak-ing into consideration on the one hand the dynamic state of condi-tions in most soils and waters, implying an almost continuous change in environmental conditions, and on the other hand the marked diversity in the nutritional requirements of various microbial species, it is clear that it is not easy to prophesy which germs will be abundant, which will maintain themselves at a low numerical level, and which will die off in a special locale at a certain moment.

That nevertheless the microbiologist so often succeeds in isolating specific microbes from a given sample of soil or water is due to a methodological principle first applied by Winogradsky,[4] and still more consciously developed with quite amazing success by my great predecessor in the Delft chair of microbiology, Beijerinck.[5] This principle has been dubbed by Beijerinck the ecological approach; its application depends on a well-considered selection of the conditions in a primary culture medium, thus causing preferential growth of a certain type of germ, ultimately leading to a predominance of the conditionally fittest. As soon as this stage is attained, isolation of the prevalent organism with the aid of methods commonly used by microbiologists is, of course, an easy affair.

Armed with this mighty tool, Winogradsky, Beijerinck, and those who followed them have made a thorough exploration of the microbe world. Besides the fact that these investigations have proved the practically ubiquitous occurrence of many microorganisms on earth, they have thrown a clear light on the surprisingly large diversity in nutritional requirements of the various microbial types. The remarkable result was obtained that nearly every soil sample seemed to contain germs willing to develop even in media with an extremely one-sided composition, for example, those containing one simple organic compound as sole source of carbon. In consequence, no sooner was one specialized microbe discovered than another with still greater achievements came to light.

The classical examples of the application of the microecological principle, usually designated as the principle of elective or enrichment culture, are, of course, well known among microbiologists. Yet it seems to me that not many are fully aware of its tremendous import. Is it not more or less a miracle that with its aid it is quite feasible to prove within a short time the wide occurrence of a microbe willing to feed on some new synthetic herbicide? [6] Or is it not quite amazing when a successful enrichment experiment shows that in an arbitrarily chosen soil sample microbes are present which are able to use carbon monoxide as sole source of carbon, especially when we take into consideration the fact that this gas so rarely occurs in nature? [7]

I think that we may expect that our "macrobiologist," on being confronted with a nearly endless diversity of such physiological monstrosities would find the microbiological scenery bewildering. On the other hand, the demonstration of the almost limitless applicability of the elective culture will make him ponder on its significance for microbial ecology. As a result he will be unable to escape the conclusion that in nature, with its continuously changing environmental conditions, successions of microbial forms will also occur. It is clear that this opens a new vision on the almost infinite capacity of life—this word used in its collective sense—for adapting itself to the immense variety of external conditions realized on earth. Is not the conclusion warranted that our "macrobiologist" has thus been forced to acknowledge the existence of potencies of life that he would never have discovered if he had stuck to his plants and animals?

However, our "macrobiologist" would certainly be most shocked by the fact that his clear notions regarding the energetic basis of life, derived from his studies of green plants and animals, had been thoroughly uprooted as a result of an acquaintance with the microbes.

Starting with the green plants he would have arrived at the conclusion that a living organism is an entity in which radiant energy is converted into chemical energy, thus enabling the organism to grow at the expense of carbon dioxide and some other simple mineral compounds. In addition he would have noticed that the utilization of the radiant energy was dependent on the presence of chlorophyll-containing cells in the plants. Next directing his attention to animals he would at first be at a loss on finding that any apparatus for an energetically important conversion of radiant energy apparently was lacking. On continuing his studies he would discover some characteristics of the animal forms of life, in particular, their need for a constant supply of free oxygen and of the dead remains of plants or of other animals.

Our "macrobiologist" would, therefore, be conversant with the idea that life had found two fully independent solutions for the problem of meeting its energetic and nutritional needs: a purely mineral nutrition provided that radiant energy can be utilized, and a nutrition depending on the availability of a complex organic food, part of which is burnt with the aid of free oxygen.

In view of all this we can understand the horror with which the "macrobiologist" would learn that there are microbes which are able to proliferate in completely inorganic media, but which, in contrast to the green plants, are not in need of radiant energy. Next he would meet with microbes that, like his animals, could use the system: organic matter plus oxygen in order to satisfy their nutritional demands. But again he would be startled when a deeper penetration into the behavior of these organisms taught him that, in contrast to what he had found for his animals, a large number of species would be perfectly happy with one single organic compound in their food. And his surprise would mount to amazement on finding that the different species showed an extreme diversity in the nature of the compound suitable for the maintenance of their life, and that among these compounds many are very remote from the normal substrates of animal nutrition. What could he think of forms of life for which, in addition to mineral salts, a substance chemically so inert as a paraffine hydrocarbon is the only requirement for proliferation? Or to make it still more paradoxical, how could our "macrobiologist" ever digest the idea that some microbes are able to accept certain phenols, so rightly renowned for their germicidal properties, as sole organic component of their food?

It seems possible that the "macrobiologist" would still find some consolation in the consideration that all these forms of life had at least one point in common with his animals, namely, the need for free oxygen which, here too, apparently was used to bring about a slow combustion of some component of the food. But scarcely having reached this conclusion, he would stumble upon various types of life that as Pasteur proved can flourish in the absence of free oxygen, and whose activities may even be inhibited by this gas.

It is easily understood that the microbiologist, so far largely occupied with an exploration of the microbe world, also began to feel the need for an inventory and subsequent evaluation of these findings, at first sight so chaotic. The first task in this respect was, of course, to draw up a survey of the various metabolic types encountered in microorganisms. A brief outline of the results obtained in these efforts to bring about a preliminary ordering follows.

From studies of the metabolism of the living cell the general experience has been gained that part of the components of the food that enter the cell are excreted again into the surrounding medium after having undergone a chemical conversion. It is usual to designate this part of metabolism as "catabolism" or "dissimilation," in contrast to those chemical conversions of food components that lead to the building up of cell constituents, and are summed up in the terms "anabolism" or "assimilation."

For reasons that will become clear later on, it is appropriate to consider the catabolic aspect of metabolism first. The foregoing definition of a dissimilatory process obviously implies that such a process can be important to the cell only from the standpoint of energy supply. And to this I may add at once that experience teaches that continuous transformation of chemical energy present in the food is an indispensable condition for maintaining the cell in an active state.

Now it has been well known since the time of Lavoisier that in animals the main dissimilatory process is a slow combustion of carbohydrates, fats, or amino acids with the aid of oxygen derived from the atmosphere, thus yielding carbon dioxide, water, and ammonia. This so-called respiration process is also encountered in the green plants, but here it is preceded by the primary energy-yielding process, the photochemical conversion of carbon dioxide and water to carbohydrate, which then acts as the substrate of respiration.

In view of the universal occurrence of the respiration process in the higher forms of life, one might expect that the microbial cell would also depend on this fundamental conversion for satisfying its energy requirements. And such has indeed been found in many different microorganisms.

However, a further investigation of the dissimilatory activities of microbes endowed with the faculty of bringing about this standard respiration process has led to some remarkable results.

In the first place it was found that in many microbial species, at least under certain, often ill-defined conditions, the oxidation of carbohydrate does not lead to the final oxidation products, carbon dioxide and water. Depending on both the specific organism and external conditions, different products of incomplete oxidation may be excreted by the cell. Table 1 lists some conversions leading to different products, all derived from the incomplete oxidation of glucose.

The second point that has emerged from the investigation of the microbial respiratory process is that for one and the same species a surprisingly large variety of chemical compounds can often serve as respiratory substrate. To cite an example: den Dooren de Jong long ago demonstrated that a strain of *Pseudomonas putida* can proliferate on a mineral medium to which any one of some 80 compounds was added as sole organic component.[8] It should be noted that these compounds include representatives of structurally quite unrelated groups.

In view of these facts it is clear that the "macrobiologist's" notion of respiration as being a more or less standardized process has to be definitely amended.

Another point of view resulting from the studies of microbial respiration is that the suitability of a compound as a substrate is not a property of the compound as such, but also depends on the specific character of the oxidizing cell. This has been previously indicated when referring to the possibility of isolating specific

TABLE 1. VARIOUS TYPES OF OXIDATIVE GLUCOSE DISSIMILATION BY MICROORGANISMS.*

$$C_6H_{12}O_6 + 6O_2 \rightarrow 6CO_2 + 6H_2O$$
carbon dioxide

$$C_6H_{12}O_6 + 5O_2 \rightarrow 2HOOC \cdot COOH + 2CO_2 + 4H_2O$$
oxalic acid

$$C_6H_{12}O_6 + 1\tfrac{1}{2}O_2 \rightarrow HOOC \cdot CH_2 \cdot C \cdot COOH + CO_2 + 3H_2O$$
$$\|$$
$$CH_2$$
itaconic acid

$$C_6H_{12}O_6 + 1\tfrac{1}{2}O_2 \rightarrow HOOC \cdot CH_2 \cdot COH \cdot CH_2 \cdot COOH + 2H_2O$$
$$|$$
$$COOH$$
citric acid

$$C_6H_{12}O_6 + O_2 \rightarrow CH_2OH \cdot CO \cdot CHOH \cdot CHOH \cdot CHOH \cdot COOH + H_2O$$
5-ketogluconic acid

$$C_6H_{12}O_6 + \tfrac{1}{2}O_2 \rightarrow CH_2OH \cdot CHOH \cdot CHOH \cdot CHOH \cdot CHOH \cdot COOH$$
gluconic acid

$$C_6H_{12}O_6 + \tfrac{1}{2}O_2 \rightarrow CH_2OH \cdot C = CH - CO - COH = CH + 3H_2O$$
$$\underline{\qquad\qquad O\qquad\qquad}$$
kojic acid

* From A. J. Kluyver, *Chemistry & Industry 1952*, 136.

microbes with the aid of the elective-culture method; depending on the nature of the organic compound added to some mineral medium, widely different microbes may come to the fore. But the extreme subtlety of this specificity is especially tangible in another observation made by den Dooren de Jong. For two closely related bacterial species, *Pseudomonas putida* and *Pseudomonas acidovorans,* he found a difference in behavior toward the homologous terms of the dicarboxylic acid series, as shown by Table 2. Is it not highly remarkable that both species oxidize the second, third, and fourth members of the series, while *Ps. putida* refuses to do so with the next five members although these are fully acceptable as respiration substrates to *Ps. acidovorans?*

Next there are the bacteria, already casually referred to that can develop in a purely mineral medium in the absence of radiant energy. To the genius of Winogradsky we owe the knowledge that representatives of various bacterial groups can thrive in the com-

TABLE 2. SPECIFICITY IN RESPIRATORY SUBSTRATES FOR TWO CLOSELY RELATED BACTERIAL SPECIES; + SUITABLE, — UNSUITABLE (after den Dooren de Jong).

Substrate	*Pseudomonas putida*	*Pseudomonas acidovorans*
oxalic acid	—	—
malonic acid	+	+
succinic acid	+	+
glutaric acid	+	+
adipic acid	—	+
pimelic acid	—	+
suberic acid	—	+
azelaic acid	—	+
sebacic acid	—	+

plete absence of light and of all organic matter, provided that both carbon dioxide and oxygen are supplied together with some oxidizable inorganic compound. Various types of these so-called chemoautotrophic bacteria have successively been discovered: the nitrifying bacteria, which oxidize ammonia or nitrite; the sulfur bacteria, which oxidize hydrogen sulfide, elementary sulfur, and some simple inorganic sulfur compounds; and finally iron bacteria, which can oxidize reduced iron compounds. Table 3 gives some idea of the remarkable conversions brought about by these types of bacteria. Is it too much to conclude that our "macrobiologist" will be dazzled when he has to accept forms of life for which the potential energy of such simple chemical systems suffices?

But we have already remarked that the microbiologist has still a bigger surprise in store. So far reference has been made only to microbes that at least had one important feature in common with animals: in all cases their energy need was evidently met by a chemical conversion in which free oxygen, normally provided by the atmosphere, took part. The demonstration that living organisms in great diversity may also abound in media wholly devoid of free oxygen must again come as a serious shock to our "macro-

TABLE 3. DISSIMILATION PROCESSES OF SOME CHEMOAUTOTROPHIC BACTERIA.*

$$
\begin{aligned}
NH_3 &+ 1\tfrac{1}{2}O_2 &&\rightarrow HNO_2 &&+ H_2O \\
HNO_2 &+ \tfrac{1}{2}O_2 &&\rightarrow HNO_3 \\
H_2S &+ \tfrac{1}{2}O_2 &&\rightarrow S &&+ H_2O \\
S &+ 1\tfrac{1}{2}O_2 + H_2O &&\rightarrow H_2SO_4 \\
Na_2S_2O_3 &+ 2O_2 + H_2O &&\rightarrow Na_2SO_4 &&+ H_2SO_4 \\
2FeCO_3 &+ \tfrac{1}{2}O_2 + 3H_2O &&\rightarrow 2Fe(OH)_3 &&+ 2CO_2 \\
H_2 &+ \tfrac{1}{2}O_2 &&\rightarrow H_2O
\end{aligned}
$$

* From *Chemistry & Industry 1952*, 136.

biologist." And he will find it especially difficult to digest the idea that at least for certain of these organisms the oxygen that is so beneficial for his higher organisms may even act as a deadly poison.

Fortunately Pasteur, the discoverer of this anaerobic life, at once keenly felt that so anomalous a situation called for some explanation, and, what is still more important, he immediately succeeded in indicating the essential characteristics of the newly discovered mode of life. Pasteur stressed that in the absence of the respiration process another energy-yielding chemical conversion should take its place, and he did not hesitate to designate as such the rather obscure processes long known as fermentation and putrefaction.

Gradually the microbiologist has succeeded in becoming acquainted with a large number of microorganisms that are able to proliferate in the absence of free oxygen, and in ascertaining the nature of the substrates required and of the products formed in their conversion.

The results of these investigations have again been more or less bewildering, with regard to the diversity both of the utilizable substrates and of the metabolic products formed. Apparently the trick of providing the anaerobic organism with the energy needed for its maintenance and proliferation has been solved in almost countless ways. Needless to say, this again opens for our "macrobiologist" quite new vistas on life's potencies.

The variety of utilizable substrates covers the entire range from naturally occurring complex compounds, such as proteins and polysaccharides, to their constituent units, the amino acids and simple sugars. Still more astounding is the fact that substances such as lactic acid, glycerol, ethanol, and even carbon monoxide have proved to be fully acceptable substrates for certain types of anaerobic microorganisms.

Depending on the type of substrate used, the dissimilatory products formed obviously show a great variation. However, even a single substrate may be decomposed to quite different products depending on the nature of the microbial species involved.

This is very clearly shown by a comparison of the dissimilatory products obtained in the fermentation of glucose, a substrate par excellence for many diverse microorganisms. Alcoholic fermentation, that is, the conversion of glucose into two molecules of ethanol and two molecules of carbon dioxide, is certainly the best-known example of such an anaerobic glucose conversion. But the study of the fermentation processes brought about by various bacterial species has left no doubt that in these processes the glucose may undergo conversions of the types collected in Table 4.

It should, however, be understood that the situation is still far more complicated than might be suggested by the table. Actually, the elementary processes shown therein are seldom encountered singly. As a rule, the number of fermentation products is large; the quantities in which these products are formed do not show stoichiometric relations; and the ratios between the various end products may vary considerably with external conditions. This extremely puzzling situation has been unraveled to the extent that it has become clear that in these cases we are dealing with mixed fermentations; in other words, some of the substrate molecules apparently undergo a conversion which differs from that to which others are subjected. This obviously explains both the ab-

TABLE 4. VARIOUS TYPES OF ELEMENTARY FERMENTATIVE GLUCOSE-DISSIMILATION PROCESSES BROUGHT ABOUT BY MICROORGANISMS.*

$C_6H_{12}O_6 \rightarrow 2CH_3 \cdot CH_2OH + 2CO_2$
ethyl alcohol

$C_6H_{12}O_6 \rightarrow 2CH_3 \cdot CHOH \cdot COOH$
lactic acid

$1\frac{1}{2}C_6H_{12}O_6 \rightarrow 2CH_3 \cdot CH_2 \cdot COOH + CH_3 \cdot COOH + CO_2 + H_2O$
propionic acid $\qquad$ acetic acid

$C_6H_{12}O_6 \rightarrow CH_3 \cdot CHOH \cdot CHOH \cdot CH_3 + 2CO_2 + H_2$
2,3-butanediol

$3C_6H_{12}O_6 \rightarrow 2CH_3 \cdot CHOH \cdot CHOH \cdot CH_3 + 2CH_2OH \cdot CHOH \cdot CH_2OH + 4CO_2$
2,3-butanediol $\qquad$ glycerol

$C_6H_{12}O_6 \rightarrow CH_3 \cdot CH_2 \cdot CH_2 \cdot COOH + 2CO_2 + 2H_2$
butyric acid

$\qquad + H_2O$
$C_6H_{12}O_6 \rightarrow CH_3 \cdot CO \cdot CH_3 + 3CO_2 + 4H_2$
acetone

$C_6H_{12}O_6 \rightarrow 3CH_3 \cdot COOH$
acetic acid

* From *Chemistry & Industry 1952*, 136.

sence of stoichiometric relations and the dependence of the results on external conditions.

Leaving this complication aside for the moment, it should be stressed that the elementary processes as such also present serious riddles to the chemical mind. On closer consideration, however, there is one characteristic that they seem to have in common, namely, that certain of the compounds formed in these conversions are reduced, while others are oxidized as compared with the substrate.

There is one type of fermentation that shows this principle in its most extreme form, namely, the so-called methane fermentation. In extension of earlier investigations, especially those of Söhngen,[9] it has been shown by Buswell and collaborators [10] that their crude cultures of methane bacteria succeeded in converting the most diverse organic compounds almost quantitatively into a

TABLE 5. SOME DISSIMILATION PROCESSES OF METHANE BACTERIA.

$4H \cdot COOH$ formic acid	$\rightarrow$	$CH_4 + 3CO_2 + 2H_2O$
$2CH_3 \cdot COOH$ acetic acid	$\rightarrow$	$2CH_4 + 2CO_2$
$4CH_3 \cdot CH_2 \cdot COOH$ propionic acid	$+ 2H_2O \rightarrow$	$7CH_4 + 5CO_2$
$2CH_3 \cdot CH_2 \cdot CH_2 \cdot COOH$ butyric acid	$+ 2H_2O \rightarrow$	$5CH_4 + 3CO_2$
$2CH_3 \cdot CHOH \cdot COOH$ lactic acid	$\rightarrow$	$3CH_4 + 3CO_2$
$4C_6H_5 \cdot COOH$ benzoic acid	$+ 18H_2O \rightarrow$	$15CH_4 + 13CO_2$
$4CH_3OH$ methanol	$\rightarrow$	$3CH_4 + CO_2 + 2H_2O$
$2CH_3 \cdot CH_2OH$ ethanol	$\rightarrow$	$3CH_4 + CO_2$
$CH_3 \cdot CO \cdot CH_3$ acetone	$+ H_2O \rightarrow$	$2CH_4 + CO_2$

mixture of the most oxidized and the most reduced form of the element carbon. A selection of over-all reactions of such conversions is found in Table 5. So many compounds have been found liable to this type of conversion that Buswell has rightly observed that methane fermentation can be represented by the following general equation:

$$C_nH_aO_b + \left(n - \frac{a}{4} - \frac{b}{2}\right) H_2O \rightarrow \left(\frac{n}{2} - \frac{a}{8} + \frac{b}{4}\right) CO_2 + \left(\frac{n}{2} + \frac{a}{8} - \frac{b}{4}\right) CH_4.$$

Still another aspect of bacterial fermentation processes seems worth stressing. It is rather usual to describe fermentation as a typical breakdown process, implying that the molecules formed are simpler than those of the substrate, thus suggesting that fermentation should be characterized by the breaking of C–C bonds. That this is not at all an essential point in fermentation is, however, clearly shown in the methane fermentation of such a simple compound as carbon monoxide, for which process Schnellen [11] found the following equation to hold:

$$4CO + 2H_2O \rightarrow 3CO_2 + CH_4.$$

Still more remarkable in this respect are perhaps the fermentation processes in which new C–C bonds are formed, so that the excreted dissimilatory products consist of larger molecules than the substrate from which they originate.

A typical example is found in Wieringa's discovery [12] of an anaerobic bacterium with the remarkable property of converting a mixture of carbon dioxide and hydrogen into acetic acid. Another perhaps still more striking example is the isolation by Barker [13] of an anaerobic bacterium able to bring about a fermentation of ethanol in which a considerable part of this substrate is converted into caproic acid.

Here we can close the description of the experiences of our "macrobiologist." In striking the balance, it seems probable that disillusion, and even despair, may well be his predominant feeling. For evidently he would have to modify most radically his ideas regarding the ways in which the energy requirements for life can be met. Neither conversion of radiant into chemical energy, nor the more or less standardized respiration process of animal physiology could be considered essential for the well-being of a living organism. Instead, a multitude of chemical conversions of an almost bewildering diversity appears to satisfy the energetic needs of the cell.

We shall now pass in review how this situation has developed owing to four decades of world-wide research, and finally make an attempt to evaluate the influence that this development has had on the biologist's outlook.

Gradually the desire to penetrate into the mysteries of dissimilatory chemistry grew stronger and stronger. It seems justified to conclude that the first successful attempt to elucidate the mechanism of a dissimilatory process was made in the study of alcoholic fermentation—the anaerobic breakdown of glucose into ethanol and carbon dioxide by baker's or brewer's yeast. Looking at the gross formula of this conversion, this is a quite incomprehensible process: we do not find the methyl group of the ethanol in the glucose, nor is there any indication from which carbon atoms the carbon dioxide is derived. The inability of even the present-day organic chemist to accomplish this conversion without the aid of the living cell or catalysts derived therefrom is eloquent testimony to the existence of a curious chemical riddle.

It would be superfluous to give here a survey of the numerous observations which in the course of thirty years have led to our present insight into this metabolic process; for the present discussion it will suffice to consider the final result, the so-called Embden-Meyerhof scheme (Fig. 1), which makes it clear that the solution of the riddle of the conversion is to be found in the existence of a chain of not less than 12 specifically catalyzed step reactions, most of which are reversible.

The most remarkable feature of the scheme as a whole is undoubtedly that all these primary reactions evidently belong to one of two types. Apparently we are dealing either with the transference of a phosphate group from one molecule to a second one (or from one part of a molecule to a second part), or with a coupled dehydrogenation and hydrogenation in which hydrogen atoms are transferred in an analogous way. It is also worth noticing that the fermentation of one molecule of glucose is indissolubly connected with the formation of two molecules of adenosine triphosphate (ATP) out of two molecules of adenosine diphosphate (ADP). This implies that sugar fermentation is

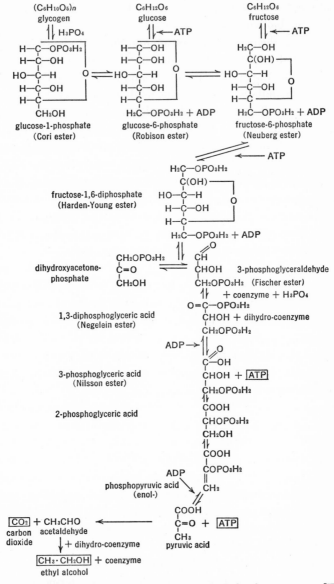

Fig. 1. The Embden-Meyerhof scheme for alcoholic fermentation. [From *Chemistry & Industry 1952*, p. 136.]

coupled with a stoichiometric consumption of a second compound, a point to which I shall return later on.

The successful unraveling of the mechanism of alcoholic fermentation—which in later stages became meshed with investigations on the mechanism of glycolysis in muscle—has materially contributed to the elucidation of the mechanism of the normal respiration process, in which glucose is oxidized to carbon dioxide and water. Currently it seems that the initial conversions of glucose during its oxidation are often the same as those encountered in alcoholic fermentation and glycolysis. However, the pyruvic acid enters into a different pathway; a series of reactions—involving a decarboxylation and a dehydrogenation—leads to a coupling of the acetyl residue with oxalacetic acid and in doing so this residue enters into the so-called Krebs or tricarboxylic acid cycle (Fig. 2). In this cycle four more dehydrogenation reactions occur, while two carbon dioxide molecules are split off, and ultimately the oxalacetic acid is regenerated. In the five dehydrogenation reactions the hydrogen is always primarily transferred to the coenzyme of the dehydrogenase; from this reduced compound it passes along a chain of respiratory catalysts at the end of which oxygen acts as the final acceptor, as illustrated in Fig. 3.

The most important result of this analysis is, however, that it clearly shows a remarkable conformity between the processes of alcoholic fermentation and respiration, remote as these may seem at first sight, since evidently in both processes the reaction

$$AH_2 + B \rightarrow A + BH_2$$

plays an essential role. The difference between the two appears to be restricted to the fact that in respiration the molecule B, which acts as the ultimate hydrogen acceptor, is free oxygen, while in fermentation this acceptor B is some organic compound derived from the substrate itself.

We shall postpone a discussion of the far-reaching implications of this result till we have examined the evolution of our knowledge regarding the mechanism of various other microbial fermen-

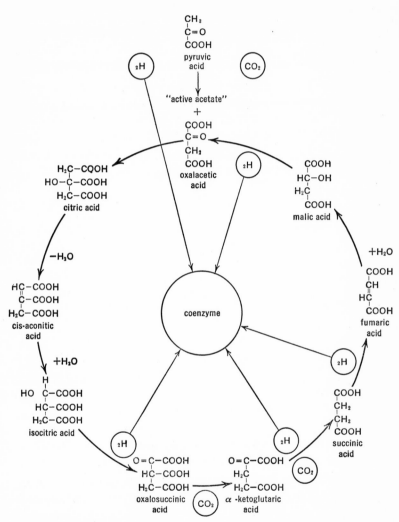

Fig. 2. The Krebs or tricarboxylic acid cycle in respiration. [From *Chemistry & Industry 1952*, p. 136.]

tations of glucose, which processes—as we have already remarked
—as a rule are characterized by the formation of a large number
of fermentation products in quantities that are subject to large
variations.

A remarkable exception to this rule is the dissimilation of the

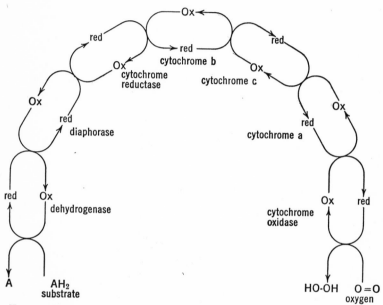

Fig. 3. The final phase of hydrogen transport in respiration.

so-called homofermentative lactic acid bacteria. Here we meet
with a conversion that as a first approximation is confined to a
splitting of glucose into two molecules of lactic acid. The practical identity of this process with muscle glycolysis is evident, and
this explains why it was soon proved that the initial conversions
of the glucose are the same as in alcoholic fermentation. But in
lactic acid fermentation the pyruvic acid formed is not decarboxylated; instead it undergoes a direct hydrogenation reaction leading to the sole fermentation product, lactic acid.

Next we consider the so-called butyric acid fermentation, which shows a somewhat more complex picture. Here the dissimilatory products are mainly restricted to butyric acid, acetic acid, carbon dioxide, and hydrogen, but experience shows that there may occur considerable variations in the quantitative relations of these compounds.

Experimental evidence to date supports an interpretation according to Fig. 4.

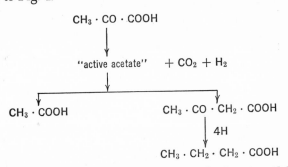

$$CH_3 \cdot CO \cdot COOH$$

$$\text{"active acetate"} \quad + CO_2 + H_2$$

$$CH_3 \cdot COOH \qquad CH_3 \cdot CO \cdot CH_2 \cdot COOH$$

$$4H$$

$$CH_3 \cdot CH_2 \cdot CH_2 \cdot COOH$$

Fig. 4. Over-all reactions in glucose fermentation by butyric-acid bacteria. The pyruvic acid, along with transferable hydrogen, is produced as in alcoholic fermentation.

Apart from indicating by what step reactions the end products are believed to arise, this scheme also shows how variations in the ratio of the end products may occur, since a degradation product of pyruvic acid—indicated in the scheme as "active acetate"—is assumed to give rise to both acetic and butyric acid. If acetic acid is formed, hydrogen is eliminated as molecular hydrogen; in the case of butyric acid formation the hydrogen is partly used for the hydrogenation of the final product of the condensation of two "active acetates," namely, acetoacetic acid. We need, therefore, only accept that the fate of the "active acetate" at the crossroads is influenced by external conditions, such as temperature, pH, etc., to be no longer shocked by the conspicuous quantitative variation in the ratio of the final products.

Thus prepared, we are also able to attack the problem of the still more complicated dissimilatory process of the closely related butyl alcohol-producing bacteria. Here we meet again with the four products of butyric acid fermentation, but in addition ethanol, butanol, acetone, and sometimes isopropanol are produced, all in far from negligible quantities. Experimental evidence is in favor of the view that the formation of all these products proceeds in the ways indicated in Fig. 5.

The most remarkable feature of this scheme is undoubtedly that we meet here with several crossroads in the metabolic pathway.

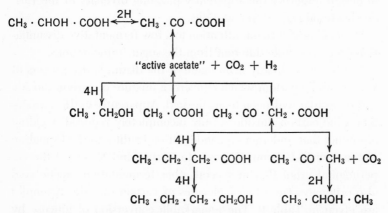

Fig. 5. Over-all reactions in glucose fermentation by butyl alcohol bacteria. The pyruvic acid and transferable hydrogen are produced as in alcoholic fermentation.

"Active acetate" may undergo a hydrogenation to ethanol; it may yield acetic acid; and finally it may be subject to a condensation reaction leading to acetoacetic acid. This compound in its turn can undergo either a decarboxylation yielding acetone and its hydrogenation product, isopropanol, or a hydrogenation leading to butyric acid and its hydrogenation product, butanol. A considerable variation in the quantitative relations of the final products is, therefore, easily understood.

It would carry us too far to review here all other known types of bacterial glucose fermentations. I will just mention two more examples, namely, the glucose fermentations brought about by

Escherichia coli and by *Aerobacter aerogenes*. In the first case we meet with succinic acid, in the second case in addition with 2, 3 butanediol as a new fermentation product. It may suffice to state that the available evidence suggests that these final metabolic products too are linked with the substrate by a chain of elementary reactions all belonging either to the phosphate- or to the hydrogen-transferring type.

The conclusion seems warranted that a quite comforting unity in design underlies the apparently puzzling diversity of the various bacterial sugar fermentations.

We shall next turn our attention to a few fermentative dissimilation processes quite different from the sugar fermentations.

Mention has already been made of the dissimilatory process of Wieringa's bacterium which converts a mixture of carbon dioxide and molecular hydrogen to acetic acid. Apparently in this fermentation the carbon dioxide is only incompletely reduced, yielding a product that undergoes a condensation leading to the formation of the new C–C bond. We owe to Barker and Kamen [14] the experimental proof that in several other fermentations acetic acid also originates from two molecules of carbon dioxide. Examples are given in Table 6. The remarkable conversion of glucose by *Clostridium aceticum* into three molecules of acetic acid is deserving of special attention.

Although in these various cases the detailed mechanism of the process is still obscure, it is difficult to escape the conclusion that here too an incomplete hydrogenation of carbon dioxide—this time with hydrogen derived from the substrate—precedes the coupling of the two carbon atoms, implying that the coupled dehydrogenation and hydrogenation is again the predominant feature of the process.

I now come to a most notable set of dissimilatory processes, which are characterized by the common property that various organic substrates are able to sustain the anaerobic life of the cell only if some simple inorganic compound is also present in significant quantity. I refer to the processes that are best designated as true dissimilatory nitrate, sulfate, and carbonate reduction.

Among these the process of nitrate reduction has been known for a very long time. As early as 1886 the French investigators Gayon and Dupetit conclusively proved that there are bacteria which can thrive in a medium containing an organic substrate

TABLE 6. OVER-ALL REACTIONS OF FERMENTATIONS DEPENDING ON THE FORMATION OF ACETIC ACID OUT OF CARBON DIOXIDE.*

General equation
$$4H_2A + 2CO_2 \rightarrow 4A + CH_3 \cdot COOH + 2H_2O$$

Clostridium aceticum
$$4H_2 + 2CO_2 \rightarrow CH_3 \cdot COOH + 2H_2O \quad \text{(Wieringa reaction)}$$
$$C_6H_{12}O_6 + 2H_2O \rightarrow 2CH_3 \cdot COOH + 2CO_2 + 8H$$
$$8H + 2CO_2 \rightarrow CH_3 \cdot COOH + 2H_2O$$
$$\overline{C_6H_{12}O_6 \rightarrow 3CH_3 \cdot COOH}$$

Clostridium acidi-urici
$$C_5H_4O_3N_4 + 7H_2O \rightarrow 5CO_2 + 4NH_3 + 6H$$
$$6H + 1.5CO_2 \rightarrow 0.75CH_3 \cdot COOH + 1.5H_2O$$
$$\overline{C_5H_4O_3N_4 + 5.5H_2O \rightarrow 0.75CH_3 \cdot COOH + 4NH_3 + 3.5CO_2}$$

Butyribacterium rettgeri
$$CH_3 \cdot CHOH \cdot COOH + H_2O \rightarrow CH_3 \cdot COOH + CO_2 + 4H$$
$$8H + 2CO_2 \rightarrow CH_3 \cdot COOH + 2H_2O$$
$$4H + 2CH_3 \cdot COOH \rightarrow CH_3 \cdot CH_2 \cdot CH_2 \cdot COOH + 2H_2O$$

* From *Chemistry & Industry 1952*, 136.

only if either free oxygen is admitted or nitrate is added to the medium. In the latter case the nitrate was evidently reduced, since at the end of the experiment the nitrate nitrogen could be recovered either as nitrite, or as nitrous oxide, molecular nitrogen, or ammonia. Evidently the hydrogen used in these hydrogenation reactions had been derived from a dehydrogenation of the organic substrate, which process, as later investigations have shown, usually leads to the ultimate dehydrogenation product, carbon dioxide.

The most probable stages through which dissimilatory nitrate reduction proceeds are given in Fig. 6.[15]

Evidently these so-called nitrate reducing bacteria are in the fortunate position of being able to satisfy their energetic needs either through the normal respiration process:

$$AH_2 + \tfrac{1}{2}O_2 \rightarrow A + H_2O,$$

or by the perfectly analogous nitrate reduction process:

$$4AH_2 + HNO_3 \rightarrow 4A + NH_3 + 3H_2O.$$

It should be admitted that the hydrogenation of the nitrate only exceptionally leads to the ultimate hydrogenation product, NH_3; more often the hydrogenation stops at the stages of nitrous oxide or molecular nitrogen.

From the beginning it has been clear that the process of sulfate reduction, first clearly described by Beijerinck, offers a strik-

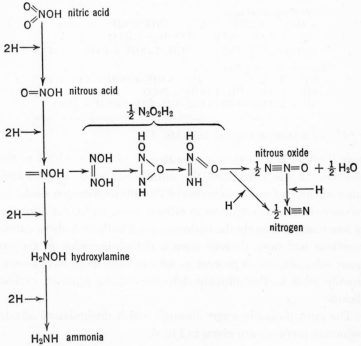

Fig. 6. Scheme of dissimilatory nitrate reduction.

ing analogy with that of nitrate reduction. However, it was found by Baars [16] that here the dehydrogenation of the substrate is often incomplete. For instance, ethanol may be oxidized anaerobically to acetic acid with simultaneous reduction of sulfate to hydrogen sulfide. This suggests that the latter conversion also proceeds stepwise; the mechanism of sulfate reduction as formulated in Fig. 7 represents a first approximation. The scheme is supported

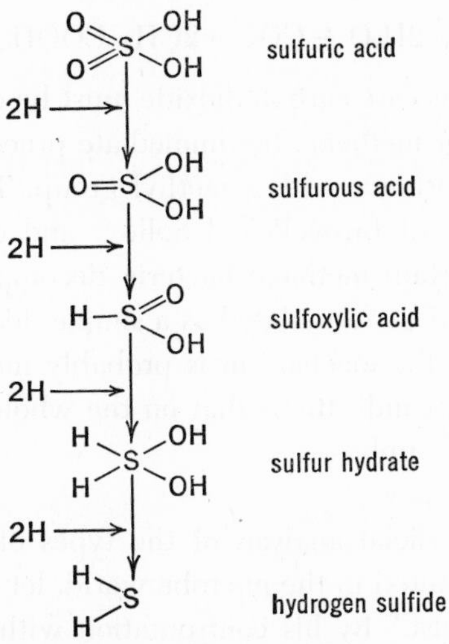

Fig. 7. Scheme of dissimilatory sulfate reduction.

by the observation that both sulfite and colloidal sulfur may replace sulfate as a hydrogen acceptor.

A striking difference between the organisms that cause sulfate and nitrate reduction, respectively, is that the former are obligately anaerobic, that is, they are unable to substitute free oxygen for sulfate in their metabolism.

The same situation holds for the process of carbonate reduction, which is also brought about by strictly anaerobic bacteria. Again in perfect analogy with the two preceding processes, these bacteria dehydrogenate various organic substrates, but this time the hydrogen is transferred to carbon dioxide which is converted into its ultimate hydrogenation product, methane.

This sharp-witted interpretation of the process long known as methane fermentation is due to van Niel, and we owe the experimental proof for the correctness of this hypothesis to Barker.[17] This investigator discovered the following extremely remarkable dissimilatory process, which for a long time to come may well remain the envy of all organic chemists:

$$2CH_3 \cdot CH_2OH + 2H_2O + CO_2 \rightarrow 2CH_3 \cdot COOH + CH_4 + 2H_2O.$$

Although in this case carbon dioxide must be considered as the ultimate source of methane, the immediate precursor of methane is probably a substance with a methyl group. This may explain the later findings of Buswell and Sollo [18] and of Stadtman and Barker [19] that certain methane bacteria decompose acetate in a manner that could be formulated as a simple decarboxylation, although in reality the mechanism is probably more complex. Yet there are sufficient indications that on the whole van Niel's general concept does apply.

After this superficial analysis of the types of energy-yielding processes encountered in the microbe world, let us now return to our "macrobiologist." By his confrontation with these incontestable facts his original ideas on the energetic basis of life will inevitably have been thoroughly uprooted. After the first shock of surprise had been overcome, it must have been a joyous revelation to him to realize that life's potencies exceed to an almost incredible extent the notion he had formed on the basis of his experiences with the higher forms of life. However, at first sight the extreme diversity of the chemical systems able to support life seems only to add to the mystery of life as a phenomenon. The feeling of discouragement that might well take possession of him will, however, subside on his becoming acquainted with the results obtained in a first analysis of the very diverse chemical conversions exploited by the various microbes to meet their energy demands. For I hope that the survey given will have convinced the reader that an analysis of this great diversity reveals a fundamental unity which tends to comfort those who struggle for insight.

It is especially the studies that have penetrated into the fermentation processes, apparently so inscrutable, which have shown that the elementary reactions which together constitute these

TABLE 7. THE PRINCIPLE OF TRANSHYDROGENATION AS THE ESSENCE OF DISSIMILATION PROCESSES.*

$$AH_2 + B \rightarrow A + BH_2$$

Fermentation
$$AH_2 \cdot B \rightarrow A + BH_2$$

Respiration
$$AH_2 + \tfrac{1}{2}O_2 \rightarrow A + OH_2$$

Nitrate reduction
$$4AH_2 + HNO_3 \rightarrow 4A + NH_3 + 3H_2O$$

Sulfate reduction
$$4AH_2 + H_2SO_4 \rightarrow 4A + SH_2 + 4H_2O$$

Carbonate reduction
$$4AH_2 + H_2CO_3 \rightarrow 4A + CH_4 + 3H_2O$$

* From *Chemistry & Industry 1952*, 136.

processes are mainly of the hydrogen transference type, for which the name of transhydrogenation is indicated.

The scheme given in Table 7 seems most appropriate to illustrate this statement. In this scheme the symbol AH_2 represents any substrate amenable to dehydrogenation. The hydrogen acceptor B in the standard reaction may be some organic compound as in fermentation, or free oxygen as in respiration, or some inorganic compounds containing N, S, or C, which are usually converted into the ultimate hydrogenation stages of these elements.

It is true that besides these transhydrogenation reactions we have also met with reactions in which phosphate groups are transferred from one molecule to a second, and which therefore are evidently closely interwoven with the transhydrogenations. Their significance seems to be twofold. In the first place the introduction of a phosphate group may make a substrate more liable to a reaction of the transhydrogenation type, as, for instance, in the introductory reactions of sugar fermentation and respiration. On the other hand we should not overlook the incontestable evidence that transhydrogenation reactions may in their turn give rise to the introduction of a phosphate group into some organic compound. It is the imperishable merit of Lipmann [20] to have clearly shown that this linking of a phosphorylation with a transhydrogenation prevents the degradation to heat of the energy liberated in this reaction. Instead, a compound is formed that, owing to its "energy-rich" phosphate bond, can enter into reactions in which the nonphosphorylated counterpart cannot function.

There is now good reason to consider that a further analysis will show that in other dissimilatory processes too these conversions will yield compounds with an "energy-rich" phosphate bond.

It even seems extremely probable that we may regard the formation of such phosphorylated compounds—which have proved to be indispensable for the synthesis of many cell constituents—as the ultimate significance of the otherwise so mysterious continuous flow of hydrogen atoms that appears to be essential for the maintenance of life. We shall consider this point further in the next chapter.

2

Microbial metabolism; further evidence for life's unity

A. J. KLUYVER

In the first chapter I have given a bird's-eye view of the diverse dissimilatory processes encountered in the microbe world. In addition I have attempted to make an analysis of these processes, and to point out that the results obtained must be most revealing to the general biologist who wishes to penetrate into the mysteries enshrouding the energetic basis of life.

However, I am fully aware that several of the elementary reactions postulated in the various schemes will have been judged by the critical reader to be speculative, and insufficiently supported by factual observations. It even seems probable that some biochemists who have concentrated their efforts on some special elementary step included in one of the schemes will have direct experimental proof that the situation is far more complicated than, or even different from, the situation suggested by the scheme in question.

Confronted with such criticism I can only give in, and remark that I have no doubt that my critics will be right. I have to confess that, indeed, my survey did not intend to be more than a first approximation to reality. The conclusions presented were reached before 1940, and the results of another 15 years of intensive and ever-expanding research have scarcely been considered. It seems, therefore, to be my duty to dwell for some moments on the main aspects of the progress made, and to answer the question how far these recent developments affect the conclusions drawn earlier.

But before doing this, it should be acknowledged that in recent

31

years the studies on microbial metabolism have become more and more intermingled with analogous studies on animal metabolism. More particularly, various tissue homogenates have proved to be equally useful biochemical tools as specific unicellular organisms; I need only mention Lipmann's famous pigeon-liver homogenate. This means, of course, that I cannot claim that recent progress should be considered to be an exclusive contribution of the microbe. Nevertheless, in many cases observations on microbial metabolism have given the impetus to important developments. In this respect it is symptomatic that modern views on the importance of transacetylation find their origin in Lipmann's keen observation on the formation of acetyl phosphate during carbohydrate breakdown by a lactic acid bacterium when tortured with free oxygen. And although in the further development of this subject most of the credit should go to the pigeon liver, yet the insight into the mechanism of the reactions involved has certainly been greatly promoted by correlated observations on the metabolism of some microorganisms.

At this stage I must make a few general remarks on the appropriateness of microbes for metabolic studies. Their ready availability in the form of pure cultures offers, of course, many advantages, especially since for the adept this implies the possibility of working with perfectly homogeneous cell suspensions on any desired scale. Moreover, as a rule, enzyme preparations can easily be obtained from the microbial cells.

But the main reason why microbes are such useful tools in the hands of the general biochemist seems to me to be the diversity in metabolism so characteristic of the microbe world. There cannot be any doubt that a great number of biochemical conversions are widely distributed among numerous cell types, both microbes and higher organisms. But there are many microbes in which a certain conversion occupies a predominant position. An example may illustrate this point. In principle it should be possible to study fatty acid synthesis with almost any cell, but it is clear that it is of great advantage to use in these studies microbes that have the remarkable property of producing in a dissimilatory process large amounts of fatty acids from a simple substrate, as Barker's bacterium produces butyric and caproic acids from ethanol.

I shall now discuss some results obtained in metabolic research during the last 15 years. Clearly, within the scope of these lectures no attempt at completeness can be made; it must suffice to indicate some of the main trends in the development.

As is well known, a great deal of the progress is due to the introduction of tracers into the study of microbial metabolism. Perhaps the most important result of the application of this new tool has been the convincing demonstration that all microbes tested, and probably we may say all living cells, have the capacity to draw carbon dioxide into their metabolism. In the pretracer era some instances had gradually accumulated that violated the generally accepted rule that carbon dioxide should be considered a biochemically almost unassailable molecule, and that its assimilation was restricted to the photo- and chemoautotrophic cells. The carbon dioxide consumption established in 1936 by Wood and Werkman in the fermentation of glycerol by a propionic acid bacterium offered a most striking example. Indications that this phenomenon would be of a much more general occurrence were present, but in a lecture read in 1939 in Helsinki I thought it safe to express myself on this subject in the following cautious terms: "For the moment a lecturer will still meet with energetic protest if he pronounces that the cattle in the pasture, or even his audience, assimilates carbon dioxide. And yet the temptation to make such a statement is already there." In the next two years the introduction of either radioactive or stable carbon isotopes in metabolic studies irrefutably established that, indeed, in the cells of very diverse heterotrophic microbes, as well as in those of animals, the carbon dioxide molecule also lacked the high degree of biochemical invulnerability which had so long been attributed to it.

Nowadays it is fully agreed that we too are endowed with the ability to incorporate carbon dioxide-carbon into organic molecules. However, the far-reaching consequences of the discovery of the heterotrophic carbon dioxide assimilation are, perhaps, not generally understood.

It should be realized that this discovery spoils one of the favorite conceptions of our "macrobiologist," his idea of a rational carbon cycle in nature, in which the green plants, owing to absorbed radiant energy, lift the carbon from the inorganic to the organic level, while the heterotrophic organisms—animals and microbes —fill the resulting gap by returning the organic compounds to the carbon dioxide state. It is clear that so sharp a division of tasks cannot be maintained, and the biologist will have to reckon with numerous small carbon cycles besides nature's main cycle.

There is, however, a second important aspect of the discovery of heterotrophic carbon dioxide assimilation that requires consideration. In the first decades of research on microbial metabolism the dogma prevailed that dissimilatory processes were, at least as far as final products were concerned, one-way conversions; carbon dioxide once formed was lost for the "metabolic game." It will be clear that this dogma implied a considerable simplification for all efforts to analyze the metabolic pathways. The convincing demonstration of the reversibility of certain decarboxylation reactions has greatly promoted the insight that the vast majority of the preceding metabolic steps are reversible as well.

Some documentation for this statement may be given. In the sugar fermentation by bacteria of the genus *Aerobacter* acetic acid had long been considered an unassailable final product of dissimilation. However, Slade and Werkman [1] proved conclusively that, if some carboxyl-labeled acetic acid was added to a medium in which *Aerobacter indologenes* was fermenting glucose, a considerable part of the labeled carbon was recovered in other fermentation products, such as 2,3-butanediol. A glance at Fig. 8 shows that the added acetic acid must have been traveling far

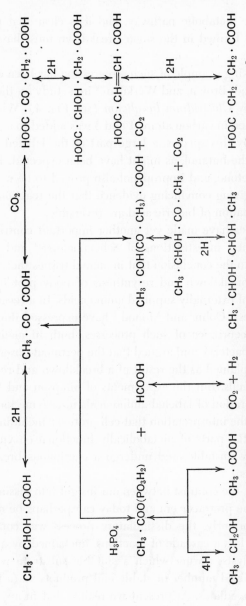

Fig. 8. Over-all reactions in glucose fermentation by *Aerobacter aerogenes*. The pyruvic acid and transferable hydrogen are produced as in alcoholic fermentation.

35

back along the metabolic pathway, and it is clear that part of the acetic acid formed in the sugar breakdown must have been doing the same.

Another striking example of such a regression has been demonstrated by Wood, Brown, and Werkman [2] in a study on the sugar fermentation by *Clostridium butylicum* (see Fig. 4). When butyric acid labeled in carbon atoms 1 and 3 was added to a glucose fermentation by this species, a large part of the labeled carbon was found in the butanol, as might have been expected. But the acetic acid, acetone, and isopropanol also proved to be markedly labeled, thus giving convincing evidence that the reactions leading to the formation of butyric acid are reversible.

Tracer studies have made yet another important contribution. The fundamental investigations of Schoenheimer [3] and Rittenberg have led to the conclusion that in animal tissues there occurs a continuous breakdown and resynthesis of body proteins with incorporation of externally supplied amino acids. In a recent publication Hogness, Cohn, and Monod [4] have expressed doubts regarding the occurrence of such processes, both in mammalian tissues and in bacteria, and argued that the pertinent observations can also be explained as the result of a breakdown and re-formation of tissue cells. But the experiments of Simpson and Velick [5] on the incorporation of labeled amino acids in enzyme molecules seem to favor the interpretation that cell proteins, including those that are essential parts of metabolically functional enzymes, are quite generally unstable, and undergo a continuous breakdown and resynthesis.

In summary, the contrast between our insight into dissimilatory processes in the pretracer era and today can perhaps be outlined as follows. Formerly, the dissimilatory process was considered to be more or less a cascade of reactions, unchained by a system of stable catalysts, during which a suitable substrate was converted into a fixed number of stable end products via a number of labile intermediates. At present we realize that in an actively metabolizing cell a highly complex system of equilibrium reactions is going on. It is a characteristic of these reactions that not only the substrate but also the intermediates and the end products are continuously taking part therein, while even the catalytic systems themselves appear to be substrates for yet other conversions.

The clear light thrown on the extremely dynamic character of the living state certainly means very real progress, and it seems to me that this is another valuable present which microbial physiology has to offer to our "macrobiologist."

Nevertheless, the remark seems justified that in several cases the introduction of tracers in metabolic studies has resulted largely in a negative contribution—destruction of our conceit in accepting an insufficiently supported pathway. The trouble is that the tracer studies have revealed such a wealth of metabolic possibilities that they often fail to make a positive contribution—the sure indication of an alternative pathway. To cite an example: the fact that the labeled carbon atoms of acetic acid added to a glucose fermentation by *Aerobacter indologenes* were partly recovered in succinic acid was first interpreted as an experimental proof for the well-known Thunberg conversion. On second consideration, however, it has been emphasized that several other pathways leading from acetic acid to succinic acid are no less probable, and thus the question of the validity of Thunberg's hypothesis is left unanswered.

This does not alter the fact that the use of tracers in metabolic research has given a convincing demonstration of the dangers involved in facile generalizations. In the pretracer era it was commonly accepted that when in a bacterial sugar fermentation ethanol and carbon dioxide were formed the sugar breakdown proceeded according to the Embden-Meyerhof scheme, as in the alcoholic sugar fermentation by yeast (Fig. 9). This all the more because in the bacteria causing the fermentation the presence of several of the catalytic systems required by the scheme had been established with certainty.

Application of the C^{14} isotope in the study of these processes led in the first place to the most gratifying result that in yeast

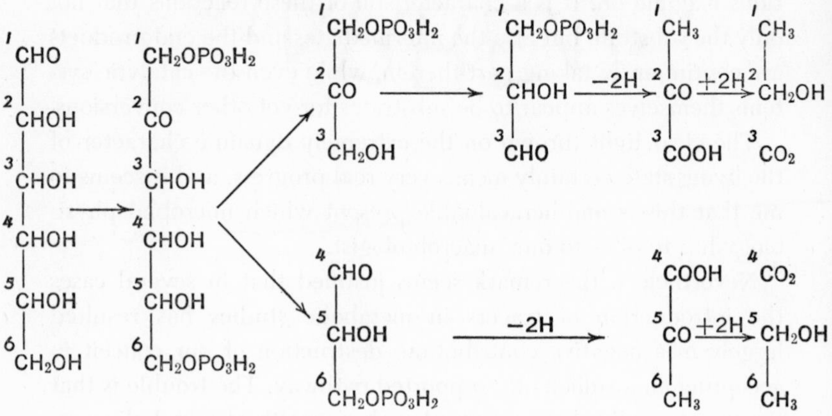

$$
\begin{array}{c}
\overset{1}{CHO} \\ |\\
\overset{2}{CHOH} \\ |\\
\overset{3}{CHOH} \\ |\\
\overset{4}{CHOH} \\ |\\
\overset{5}{CHOH} \\ |\\
\overset{6}{CH_2OH}
\end{array}
\longrightarrow
\begin{array}{c}
\overset{1}{CH_2OPO_3H_2} \\ |\\
\overset{2}{CO} \\ |\\
\overset{3}{CHOH} \\ |\\
\overset{4}{CHOH} \\ |\\
\overset{5}{CHOH} \\ |\\
\overset{6}{CH_2OPO_3H_2}
\end{array}
$$

Upper branch:

$$
\begin{array}{c}
\overset{1}{CH_2OPO_3H_2} \\ |\\
\overset{2}{CO} \\ |\\
\overset{3}{CH_2OH}
\end{array}
\longrightarrow
\begin{array}{c}
\overset{1}{CH_2OPO_3H_2} \\ |\\
\overset{2}{CHOH} \\ |\\
\overset{3}{CHO}
\end{array}
\xrightarrow{-2H}
\begin{array}{c}
\overset{1}{CH_3} \\ |\\
\overset{2}{CO} \\ |\\
\overset{3}{COOH}
\end{array}
\xrightarrow{+2H}
\begin{array}{c}
\overset{1}{CH_3} \\ |\\
\overset{2}{CH_2OH} \\ \\
\overset{3}{CO_2}
\end{array}
$$

Lower branch:

$$
\begin{array}{c}
\overset{4}{CHO} \\ |\\
\overset{5}{CHOH} \\ |\\
\overset{6}{CH_2OPO_3H_2}
\end{array}
\xrightarrow{-2H}
\begin{array}{c}
\overset{4}{COOH} \\ |\\
\overset{5}{CO} \\ |\\
\overset{6}{CH_3}
\end{array}
\xrightarrow{+2H}
\begin{array}{c}
\overset{4}{CO_2} \\ \\
\overset{5}{CH_2OH} \\ |\\
\overset{6}{CH_3}
\end{array}
$$

Fig. 9. Glucose fermentation by yeast (Embden-Meyerhof scheme).

fermentation the requisites of the Embden-Meyerhof scheme were fully met: carbon atoms 3 and 4 of the glucose molecule were mainly recovered as carbon dioxide, carbon atoms 1 and 6 as the methyl group, and carbon atoms 2 and 5 as the carbinol group of ethanol. It was, of course, tempting to postulate that the same would hold for the analogous process in bacterial fermentations.

Fortunately, however, this age has also its "sceptical biologists" and the skepticism of Gunsalus and Gibbs [6] has been well repaid. In an exemplary study of glucose fermentation by the heterolactic bacterium *Leuconostoc mesenteroides*, which yields equimolar quantities of lactic acid, ethanol, and carbon dioxide, these investigators brought convincing proof that in this fermentation only carbon atoms 2 and 3 give rise to ethanol, while the carbon dioxide is derived exclusively from carbon atom 1. Perhaps the most startling result is that the methyl group of the ethanol originates from carbon atom 2. This contrasts strongly with the results obtained in the yeast fermentation, and it is evident that in the heterolactic fermentation ethanol is the result of a markedly different metabolic pathway.

Still more shocking is the outcome of investigations reported in a recent publication by Gibbs and DeMoss [7] on the fermentation of glucose by *Zymomonas mobilis* (*Pseudomonas lindneri*), since in this fermentation—as in yeast fermentation—the metabolic products are practically confined to ethanol and carbon dioxide, lactic acid being formed in only negligible amounts. Here a generous application of variously labeled glucose preparations led to the remarkable result that the carbon dioxide arises from carbon atoms 1 and 4, the methyl group of ethanol from carbon atoms 3 and 6, and the carbinol group from carbon atoms 2 and 5. Obviously in this case the production of ethanol proceeds along yet another pathway, different from either of those in the two cases discussed above. Thus the Mexican who enjoys his alcohol in the form produced by *Z. mobilis,* that is as pulque, imbibes different carbon atoms of the fermented sugar than does the American who takes his in the form of bourbon.

It will be understood that these unexpected results have caused a flutter in the dovecot of those investigators who unremittingly search for unity in all biochemical processes. A further consideration of the results in question may, however, not be amiss. Until now the scientists engaged in these investigations have restricted themselves to suggesting some possible mechanisms whereby the observed conversions could be accomplished.

Nevertheless, it is rewarding to examine the pathways that have been suggested for these two "abnormal" alcoholic fermentations. Figure 10 gives a possible pathway for the fermentation of glucose by *Leuconostoc mesenteroides,* as suggested by Gest and Lampen.[8] It may be remarked that this scheme was largely inspired by the results obtained by these authors in their tracer studies on the fermentation of pentoses by a related lactic acid bacterium. It is clear that a primary conversion of glucose into a pentose by dehydrogenation and decarboxylation can account for the origin of the methyl group of the ethanol from carbon atom 2.

The scheme suggested by Gibbs and DeMoss for glucose fermentation by *Zymomonas mobilis* is given in Fig. 11.

The idea of an analogous primary attack on the glucose molecule is supported by the absence of aldolase in the organism. The

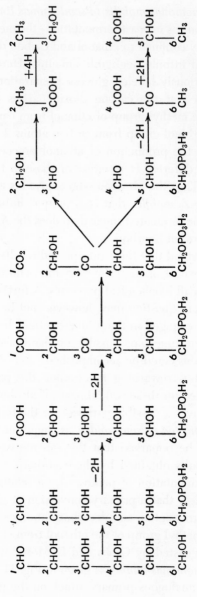

Fig. 10. Possible pathway of glucose fermentation by *Leuconostoc mesenteroides*; after Gest & Lampen.

40

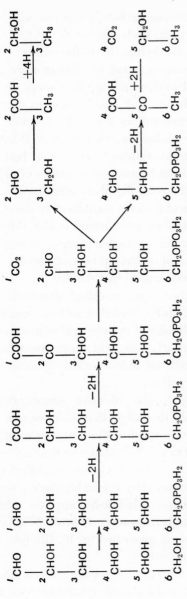

Fig. 11. Possible pathway of glucose fermentation by *Zymomonas mobilis*; after Gibbs & De Moss.

41

occurrence of the enzyme carboxylase in the cells, which is quite exceptional for bacteria, lends support to the final steps adopted.

However, we would do injustice to the authors cited if we considered these schemes as being more than mere possibilities. I have no doubt that in due time supplementary investigations on intermediate metabolism will enable them to draw up for each of the deviating fermentations a scheme as detailed and as well supported as the Embden-Meyerhof scheme. Whatever the final result may be, it seems extremely likely that both schemes will again be built up from elementary reactions of either the transhydrogenation or the transphosphorylation type.

Another example of a recent revolutionary development in our knowledge of metabolic conversions is the discovery of new pathways in the oxidative dissimilation of glucose. Here too a judicious application of tracers has been of decisive importance. In Chapter 1 it has been argued that the first phase of the oxidative conversion of glucose is the so-called glycolytic decomposition according to the Embden-Meyerhof scheme, leading to the production of two molecules of pyruvic acid which would be further oxidized via the tricarboxylic acid cycle. Nowadays there is no doubt that many cells are able to oxidize glucose along a fundamentally different pathway.[9]

We owe mainly to the extensive investigations of Cohen, Horecker, and Gibbs the insight that under certain conditions the glucose-6-phosphate formed in the introductory phosphorylation reactions is subject to a dehydrogenation reaction yielding 6-phosphogluconic acid. In its turn this compound undergoes a second dehydrogenation followed by a decarboxylation, thus producing a phosphorylated pentose, ribulose-5-phosphate, which compound is in equilibrium with its isomer, ribose-5-phosphate. As may be seen from the scheme given in Fig. 12, the fate of these compounds is quite surprising.

In the first place they are subject to a curious interaction resulting in the production of a phosphorylated heptose, sedoheptulose-7-phosphate, and of glyceraldehyde-3-phosphate. The enzyme responsible for this conversion is known as transketolase. However, the reaction products immediately enter into a second reaction which leads to fructose-6-phosphate accompanied by erythrose-4-

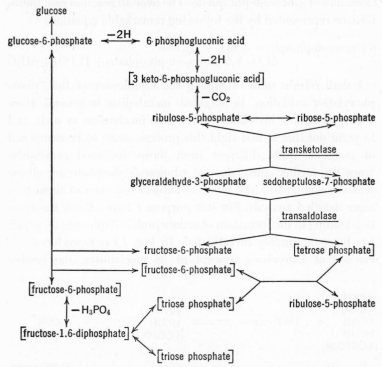

Fig. 12. Over-all reactions in glucose oxidation along the phosphorylated pathway. The occurrence of the intermediates between brackets has not yet definitely been proved.

phosphate. This reaction proceeds under the influence of a specific enzyme, transaldolase. As shown in the scheme, the tetrose phosphate is supposed to undergo a series of conversions in which one more ribulose-5-phosphate molecule is involved, with the final result that again fructose-6-phosphate is the exclusive end product. Since the latter compound is in equilibrium with glucose-6-phosphate, the starting point of the conversions, the cycle is closed.

Summarizing, we must conclude that six molecules of glucose-6-phosphate are decarboxylated to six pentose phosphate molecules which, more or less by magic, rearrange themselves to form five molecules of glucose-6-phosphate. The over-all reaction can, therefore, be represented by the following remarkable equation:

6 glucose-6-phosphate $+ 6O_2 + H_2O \rightarrow$
$$6CO_2 + 5 \text{ glucose-6-phosphate} + H_3PO_4 + 6H_2O$$

I shall refrain from discussing the significance of this "phosphorylative oxidation" in microbial metabolism in general. Here I wish to confine myself to the reaction mechanism as such, and to point out that at first sight this process seems to be composed of reactions quite different from those discussed previously. Since the further conversions of ribulose-5-phosphate are all essentially similar in kind, we shall subject only one of them to a more detailed analysis. For this purpose I have chosen the reaction leading to the formation of sedoheptulose-7-phosphate, which has been thoroughly investigated. In Fig. 13 is reproduced the essence of Horecker's concept of its mechanism; the symbol

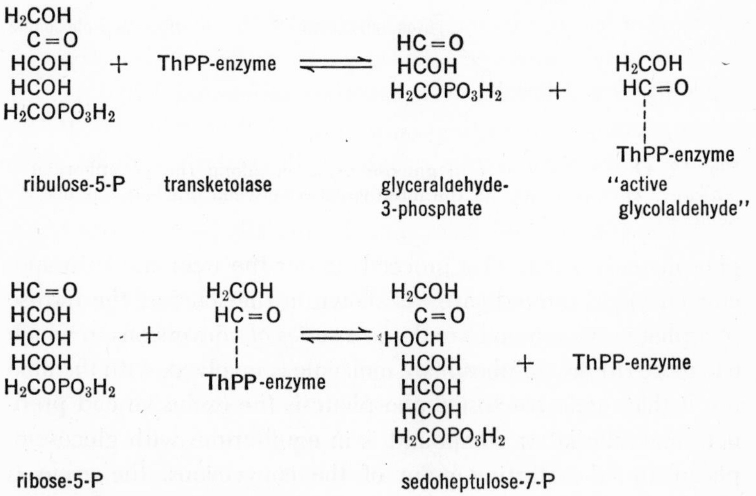

Fig. 13. The transketolase reaction.

"ThPP" denotes the catalyst, transketolase, which contains thi-amine pyrophosphate as the prosthetic group.

A closer examination of this scheme shows that the over-all re-action is composed of two steps, and it is at once evident that both are fundamentally hydrogen-transfer reactions of the types

$$AH \cdot B \rightarrow A + BH$$

and

$$AH + B \rightarrow A \cdot BH,$$

respectively. We may consequently infer that even the recognition of conspicuous differences in the manner in which sugar can be oxidatively degraded does not invalidate the general conclusions developed earlier; meanwhile we have learned, however, that "there are more paths between heaven and earth" than until re-cently had been dreamt of in the philosophy of the comparative biochemist.

Further progress in the study of metabolism has resulted from the successful outcome of attempts to penetrate into the mecha-nism of the various elementary steps that constitute the component units of the reaction schemes earlier discussed. A striking example is offered by the oxidative decarboxylation of pyruvic acid, the mechanism leading to the introduction of the acetyl group into the tricarboxylic acid cycle. So far we have characterized this de-composition as a simultaneous decarboxylation and dehydrogena-tion to a compound on the oxidation level of acetate, though, as implied by the term "active acetate," with greater reactivity.

Owing to the work of many investigators, among whom Snell, Gunsalus, O'Kane, and Reed should especially be mentioned, we know nowadays that what looks like a rather simple condensation of pyruvic acid and oxaloacetic acid to citric acid actually proceeds according to the scheme reproduced in Fig. 14.[10] From the scheme it is evident that the conversion of pyruvic acid into "active ace-tate," which can now be identified as the acetylated form of Lip-mann's coenzyme A, is in reality a chain of three consecutive re-actions. In the first place a decarboxylation occurs leading to the formation of acetaldehyde attached to the prosthetic group of

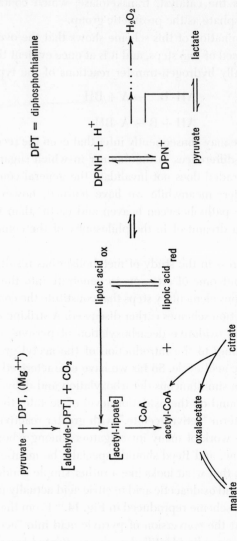

Fig. 14. The oxidative decarboxylation of pyruvic acid and its linkage with the tricarboxylic acid cycle.

the decarboxylase which has been shown to be diphosphothiamine (DPT). This complex then reacts with the oxidized form of an only recently discovered compound, α-lipoic acid, in such a way that in the new complex the aldehyde is dehydrogenated to an acetyl group (oxidation level of acetate), while the lipoic acid moiety is reduced. Next the acetyl group is transferred from the complex to Lipmann's coenzyme A with liberation of lipoic acid in the reduced state. This is again converted into the oxidized form, the hydrogen being introduced into the normal respiratory chain by the intervention of diphosphopyridine nucleotide (DPN).

It seems likely that an analogous situation will be encountered in many other metabolic reactions that until now have been considered to be elementary steps. Further research may well show these to be just gross formulations of a more or less complicated reaction chain, or show that the catalytic system involved can be separated into a coenzyme and an apoenzyme.

The last remark makes it tempting to say a few words about the significance of the discovery of a coenzyme being involved in a certain reaction step. I have to confess that my first mental reaction on hearing of such a discovery is to lower the flag to half-mast, and Table 8 may perhaps assist me in explaining why.

I imagine myself in the position of a scientist who is eager to penetrate into the mechanism of some biocatalytic conversion. Now there are two possibilities: either he arrives at the conclusion that the catalyst involved is nothing but some specific protein, as is true in many biochemical processes, or he finds that a specific coenzyme also plays a role. In the latter case he has to isolate this compound, and to establish its configuration, a task that usually is beset with considerable difficulties. And what are the consequences, if our biochemist successfully solves this problem? As shown in Table 8, at first sight there does not seem to be much reason for rejoicing. For convincing evidence has been given that the biocatalytic conversion chosen for study is, in reality, composed of two conversions, or, in other words, that another step has to be included in the reaction chain. But still worse is the realization that each of these separate steps is determined by its own specific catalyst, which implies that the poor biochemist who has started to solve one riddle is confronted with the necessity of solving two riddles!

TABLE 8. PRINCIPLE OF COENZYME ACTIVITY. DRAWBACKS.

$$AX + B \xrightarrow[\substack{\text{enzyme} \\ \text{system}}]{} A + BX$$

enzyme system = apoenzyme + coenzyme

$$AX + \text{coenzyme} \xrightarrow[\text{apoenzyme I}]{} \text{coenzyme X} + A$$

$$\text{coenzyme X} + B \xrightarrow[\text{apoenzyme II}]{} \text{coenzyme} + BX$$

Examples

	apoenzyme I	*apoenzyme II*
(a)	triosephosphate } dehydrogenase }	{ aldehyde { reductase
(b)	transphosphorylase	phosphokinase
(c)	transacetylase	acetokinase

Results
1. A new step has been included in the reaction chain
2. Instead of one, two catalytic processes have to be explained

I can also formulate it in this way, that the discovery of a co-enzyme involves the danger that uncritical minds may lose sight of the fact that the mystery of biocatalysis still hovers about the inscrutable protein in the background, the apoenzyme.

Now it will be clear that I should not have dared to make these remarks in the birthplace of coenzyme A, if I were not certain that its discoverer is as aware of this situation as I am, and more particularly if it did not present a more inspiriting side. And this aspect, which is of tremendous importance and gives us all reason to fly the flag at the top of the mast, is admirably expressed in Fig. 15, which is directly borrowed from one of Professor Lipmann's publications.[11]

From this figure we see at once that the real importance of co-enzyme A is that it acts as an intermediate in a large number of different reactions, which implies that it is a point of junction for numerous metabolic pathways. In the street plan of the cell the coenzyme fulfills the function of a square like Piccadilly Circus in London! And it is well known that big cities are best remembered by the names of their great squares.

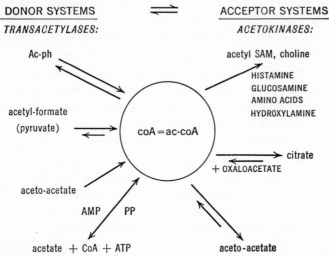

Fig. 15. The action of coenzyme A as an intermediate in different reactions (from Lipmann).

Evidently the same holds for compounds like di- and triphosphopyridine nucleotide (DPN and TPN) and adenosine triphosphate (ATP).

In addition I venture to give as my opinion that the time has arrived to abolish for cofactors of this type the derogatory name coenzyme. This name is distinctly misleading, as follows directly from the fact that nobody has ever heard of an enzyme A. The introduction of a designation such as "centrabolite" for the compounds in question might well lead to a better visualization of the biochemical structure of the cell.

So far I have been considering only how the microbe has contributed to biology by its demonstration of the general principle underlying the apparently diverse ways in which life has solved the problem of providing for its indispensable energy requirements. It is clear that in doing so I have confined myself to just one part of microbial metabolism, to wit, the dissimilatory processes. It should, however, be realized that the true greatness of metabolism manifests itself in the assimilatory processes, in which part of the food components entering the cell are converted into new cell constituents in their almost endless diversity. Evidently this is the one condition for proliferation of the cell.

It seems to me that the studies performed, especially in the last two decades, on this assimilatory phase of microbial metabolism have also yielded results of general significance that cannot be ignored with impunity by our "macrobiologist."

For a documentation of this statement I may first mention the extensive studies made in the field of microbial nutrition. Around the turn of the century it had already become clear that the nutritional demands of the various microbes differ greatly. On the one hand there were the chemoautotrophic bacteria discovered by Winogradsky, which can grow in a simple synthetic medium containing only some mineral compounds. On the other hand the medical bacteriologists had to recognize that several bacteria pathogenic for man and animal are most exacting in their demands, and can thrive only in very complex media, approaching the composition of their natural environment in the host animal. In rare cases all attempts to cultivate the organism outside the host have failed.

The majority of microbes hold an intermediate position between these extremes; here again the "macrobiologist" is confronted with an almost bewildering diversity.

In the late thirties a stream of investigations led to a careful analysis of the nutritional requirements of a great number of microbes. Insofar as these studies pertain to the dissimilatory processes they have been dealt with in the first chapter, and I shall now restrict myself to those requirements obviously connected with the building up of cell components. As such the proteins, being life's substratum, require special consideration. It has become clear that the requirements for protein synthesis cover the entire range from the need for simple inorganic nitrogen compounds to that for complex mixtures of the protein building stones, the amino acids. In later years some cases have been reported in which even simple peptides seem at least to favor protein synthesis.

But in spite of the wide differences in synthetic ability of various microorganisms, it has been established that—apart from occasional and as yet inadequately corroborated reports to the contrary—the microbial proteins always contain the same 22 amino acids that have been isolated from the proteins of the higher organisms. Nowadays, we are used to considering this as self-evident, but, in view of the very diverse origin of these proteins, such a result could scarcely have been predicted. In any case the investigations mentioned have resulted in the establishment of a most gratifying unity in life's substratum. Elizabeth Work's discovery [23] that hydrolysates of many bacteria and bluegreen algae contain, in addition to the normal amino acids, diaminopimelic acid, apparently not found in hydrolysates of other organisms, does not detract from this conclusion.

In addition, the studies on microbial metabolism have led to another development of great importance. Gradually it became clear that many microbes had nutritional demands which obviously were connected neither with the energy supply, nor with the material needs of protein synthesis, and which could be satisfied by small amounts of cell extracts. I need not discuss how an analysis of this remarkable phenomenon has shown that in all cases studied the demands could be referred to a need for one, or for a mixture of a few, organic compounds of very specific configuration. As a rule it has been possible to elucidate the configuration of these so-called growth factors or essential metabolites, whose presence in the medium in often incredibly small quantities may decide between life or death of the microbial cell. It is well known that this development took place hand in hand with an analogous development in our knowledge of animal nutrition, namely, the discovery of the animal's need for vitamins and the identification of these entities. It is also common knowledge that these parallel developments have led to the conclusion that many of the microbial growth factors are identical with vitamins required by animals.

It is, however, open to doubt whether the implications of this finding are fully realized. It is true that physiologists have readily grasped the opportunity to use microbes as tools for the detection and quantitative determination of a certain vitamin in natural materials, and the isolation of vitamin B_{12} is here to testify to the success of this way of approach. But too seldom is the main significance of the insight attained duly stressed. It is obviously of great biological importance to realize that the food deficiencies of animals are not isolated phenomena characteristic for these special forms of life, but that exactly the same situation is encountered in very remote groups of organisms. To cite an example: for Hutner it must have been an enthralling moment when he established that the same principle which in so minute a quantity protects him from the horrors of pernicious anemia also determines the well-being of the phytoflagellate *Euglena gracilis*. And to this example many others could be added. Together they constitute another argument in favor of a striking unity underlying very different forms of life.

However, this is only a first contribution of the microbes to a better comprehension of nutrition. The wide distribution of the phenomenon of food deficiency in living nature strongly suggested that the growth factors which in so small an amount remove the deficiency will play an essential role in cell metabolism. We owe mainly, although not exclusively, to studies on microbial metabolism the elucidation of this point. We all know that it has been possible to assign to nearly all growth factors a function as coenzyme or cofactor for some metabolically important cell catalyst.

The understanding of the function of growth factors naturally raised the questions how so many cells could thrive without an external supply of these factors, and how the need for particular growth factors could be so haphazardly distributed even over one and the same group of organisms. This situation has led to one of the greatest discoveries in biology, a discovery to which, remarkably, no date and no discoverer's name have been attached. But one morning biochemists awoke, and there was a consensus of opinion that cells which can do without growth factors in their medium have in fact not renounced these useful tools, but differ from the growth-factor-dependent cells by their ability to synthesize the tools in question from the constituents of the medium. The validity of this thesis has only been randomly tested, but in all these cases with positive results.

Perhaps the most impressive outcome in this respect was the demonstration by O'Kane [12] that the cells of *Thiobacillus thiooxidans* that had been grown in a medium containing merely sulfur and some inorganic salts were, indeed, a real storehouse of vitamins. The presence of thiamin, riboflavin, nicotinic acid, pantothenic acid, pyridoxin, and biotin was conclusively proved. In view of the fact that man's well-being depends on the continuous supply of each of these compounds, which he cannot synthesize, this reveals an imposing synthetic ability of the tiny microbe.

In the meantime the main conclusion to be derived from the foregoing survey of studies on microbial growth factors is that these studies have yielded a most bracing demonstration of the unity in the divergent manifestations of life. With some exaggeration it can be said that the biochemist who examines extracts of crushed cell suspensions from the most different sources will have the greatest difficulty in identifying the source of the materials; they may as well originate from sulfur bacteria as from some pigeon's organ. Even the detection of certain biocatalysts in some extract may not be very helpful in the identification, since Postgate [13] established the presence of cytochromes in the strictly anaerobic bacterium *Desulfovibrio desulfuricans,* a strange occurrence of respiratory heavy-metal catalysts in anaerobic cells producing streams of hydrogen sulfide!

The insight acquired into the diversity of the compounds that act as components of the catalytic systems active in the living cell also throws a clear light on the tremendous task with which the cell has to cope in the assimilatory part of its metabolism. Taking account of the results of chemical analyses of the material basis of life one might at first sight be impressed by the quantitative preponderance of compounds belonging to the classes of carbohydrates, lipids, and proteins. We now realize that besides the already enormous task of synthesizing compounds representative of these groups, numerous other compounds of very divergent types must also be built up.

It seems worth while to survey briefly the progress made in an understanding of this mysterious chemistry which enables a bacterium like *Thiobacillus thiooxidans* to synthesize this host of cell components from carbon dioxide and some inorganic compounds. The fact that other cells need some of these components ready-made or in the form of specific precursors only contributes to a certain simplification of the general picture without affecting its essence.

It should be said that until 1940 insight into the assimilatory processes was very restricted. It was usual to stress the energy-requiring nature of these processes, and to point out that they could only proceed owing to the simultaneous occurrence of the energy-yielding processes.

Although we are still far removed from a complete picture of the multitudinous aspects of assimilation, considerable progress has been made in the last fifteen years. The main contributions in this field have been made at Harvard by Professor Lipmann and his collaborators. Therefore I need not dwell upon this part of the subject, although I cannot ignore their main results without seriously distorting my narrative.

The first great contribution is undoubtedly the discovery of the general occurrence in the living cell of a number of phosphorylated organic compounds which are characterized by the high decrease of free energy that accompanies the splitting off of the phosphate group. This is true, for instance, of the mixed anhydrides of carboxylic and phosphoric acids, as also for the anhydride of phosphoric acid itself, pyrophosphoric acid. The main point of interest is, however, that in the dissimilatory processes certain elementary reactions of the oxidoreduction type lead to the formation of such energy-rich phosphate compounds. In the scheme of alcoholic fermentation we have met with two such reactions, resulting in the formation of 1,3-diphosphoglyceric acid and enolphosphopyruvic acid, respectively. The great significance of their formation is the fact that the energy resulting from the coupled dehydrogenation and hydrogenation is not liberated as heat, but, according to the current terminology, is stored in the newly formed "energy-rich phosphate bond." This is therefore of great importance for the economy of the cell, because the phosphate group may be transferred with little loss of free energy to other compounds. This can be a compound with intermediary function like adenylic acid that is ultimately converted into adenosin triphosphate (ATP), in which two of the phosphate groups are of the energy-rich type. And in its turn ATP can transfer these phosphate groups to some organic compound that in the phosphorylated state is then able to perform condensations which in the absence of the energy-rich phosphate bonds could not proceed.

All this means, of course, that a material link has been found between the energy-yielding dissimilatory processes and the apparently energy-requiring assimilatory processes. Hence the latter processes have been largely freed from the mystery in which they had been enshrouded for such a long time.

In this connection it is important to realize that there is now ample evidence for the concept that all dissimilatory processes, whatever their nature may be, lead to the formation of compounds with energy-rich phosphate bonds, although it has not always been possible to identify—as has successfully been done in alcoholic fermentation—the particular elementary reactions that are responsible for their formation. In consequence, reactions like alcoholic fermentation and respiration with glucose as substrate should be formulated as shown in Table 9.

It may be remarked that in the fermentative breakdown of a hexose molecule four molecules of ATP are formed, but that two of these are used up in the formation of the hexose diphosphate, leaving a net yield of two molecules of ATP. The equation for

TABLE 9. INTEGRATE FORMULATION OF THE PROCESSES OF ALCOHOLIC FERMENTATION AND RESPIRATION; ADP, ADENOSINE DIPHOSPHATE; ATP, ADENOSINE TRIPHOSPHATE.[*]

Alcoholic fermentation
$$C_6H_{12}O_6 + 2ADP + 2H_3PO_4 \rightarrow 2C_2H_5OH + 2CO_2 + 2ATP + 2H_2O$$

Respiration
$$C_6H_{12}O_6 + 6O_2 + 36ADP + 36H_3PO_4 \rightarrow 6CO_2 + 36ATP + 42H_2O$$

[*] From *Chemistry & Industry 1952*, 136.

respiration indicates that 36 ATP molecules are formed during the oxidation of a molecule of hexose. The evidence is not yet compelling, however, and the number 36 may have to be amended in the future.

The advantage of such formulations is that they make the significance of energy-yielding processes more or less tangible.

Armed with this general principle we shall now very briefly review our knowledge regarding the synthesis of various classes of cell components.

In the first place we may conclude that the general procedure for the synthesis of carbohydrates, so often encountered as reserve products and cell-wall components, does not offer great difficulties. We need only point out the reversible character of the elementary steps that together constitute the Embden-Meyerhof scheme to realize that even complex carbohydrates can be formed, as soon as pyruvic acid or any other intermediate located higher in the scheme is present. Moreover, Utter, Lipmann, and Werkman [14] have convincingly shown that in the presence of ATP pyruvic acid can be synthesized from acetate and formate, thus permitting carbohydrate synthesis from a mixture of 2- and 1-carbon compounds.

The problem of the synthesis of lipids has to a large extent been solved by the fundamental work of Lipmann and his school on the nature and function of coenzyme A. These studies have made us familiar with the universal occurrence in living cells of reactions which may be called transacetylations, since they ultimately consist in a transference of acetyl groups from one molecule to a second one. In these processes the acetylation of coenzyme A occupies a central position; more or less specific acetyl donor-activating systems take care of the transfer of the acetyl group from the donors to coenzyme A; other specific acetyl acceptor-activating systems do the same for the transfer of the acetyl group from acetyl coenzyme A to the final acetyl acceptor. Without going into further details it should be remarked that one of the systems which can act as acetyl donor is the combination of free acetate and ATP.

The establishment of the quite general occurrence of such acetyl transfers, together with the studies of Barker and collaborators on dissimilatory fatty acid production, have led Lynen to the concept of fatty acid synthesis as reproduced in Fig. 16. Lynen [15] has given experimental proof that the synthesis of the long-chain fatty acids starts with a condensation reaction between two molecules of acetyl coenzyme A. This yields acetoacetate which after hydrogenation is condensed with another acetyl group, successive hydrogenations and acetylations leading to the long-chain fatty acids.

In the general frame of my theme it should be remarked that, although this insight is mainly due to the performance of the pigeon-liver homogenate, yet the coöperation of various types of microbes has been indispensable for the rounding off of the insight obtained. It may be added that the studies of both Bloch and Lipmann have proved conclusively that in the synthesis of steroids we are again dealing with transacetylation reactions with the active coöperation of coenzyme A.

Proceeding now to the synthesis of the third main class of cell constituents, the proteins, it is clear that there is no opportunity to give here even a superficial survey of what is known regarding

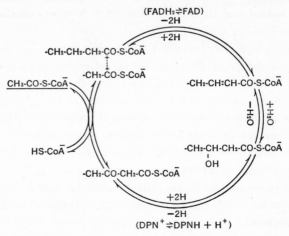

Fig. 16. Fatty acid cycle. [From F. Lynen, *Federation Proc. 12*, 683 (1953).]

the synthesis of the 22 amino acids that have been found to be the building stones of all proteins, whatever their origin. A few remarks must suffice. It has become clear that there are at least three mechanisms leading to the introduction of the amino group into some of the nitrogen-free substrates resulting from carbohydrate breakdown.

First, the mechanism long ago proposed by Knoop is undoubtedly involved in certain cases. This pathway consists of a primary reaction between an α-keto acid and ammonia yielding an imino acid which by subsequent hydrogenation is transformed into an amino acid:

$$NH_3 + R \cdot CO \cdot COOH \leftrightharpoons R \cdot COHNH_2 \cdot COOH$$
$$R \cdot CHNH_2 \cdot COOH \overset{2H}{\rightleftharpoons} R \cdot C{=}NH \cdot COOH$$

The best-known example of this type of reaction is the reductive amination of α-ketoglutaric acid, where R is $COOH \cdot CH_2 \cdot CH_2$.

Second, an important way for the introduction of NH_3 into an organic compound is the isolated case of the reversible reaction between ammonia and fumaric acid yielding aspartic acid:

$$HOOC \cdot CH = CH \cdot COOH + NH_3 \leftrightharpoons HOOC \cdot CHNH_2 \cdot CH_2 \cdot COOH$$

Finally, we owe to Braunstein the demonstration that at least certain amino acids may originate from the interaction of an α-keto acid with some amino acid, according to the equation:

$$R_1 \cdot CHNH_2 \cdot COOH + R_2 \cdot CO \cdot COOH \leftrightharpoons$$
$$R_1 \cdot CO \cdot COOH + R_2 \cdot CHNH_2 \cdot COOH$$

It should be stressed that this represents a new type of transfer mechanism, involving an amino group; this is indicated in the name "transamination" applied to this process, which nowadays is taking on increasing importance.

The manner in which the primary amino acids, aspartic and glutamic acid, themselves derived from compounds of the tricarboxylic acid cycle, act as precursors for two families of other amino acids can be illustrated by Fig. 17, borrowed from the recent penetrating tracer studies by Abelson, Roberts, et al.[16]

In addition two other important types of reactions should be discussed; in recent years these reactions have come to the fore as a consequence of detailed studies on the biosynthesis of certain amino acids. We owe to du Vigneaud [17] and his collaborators the conclusive proof that methionine often originates from a methylation of homocysteine, and that in this reaction choline can act as the methyl donor:

$$(H_3C)_3N^+ \cdot CH_2 \cdot CH_2 \cdot OH \quad + HSCH_2 \cdot CH_2 \cdot CHNH_2 \cdot COOH$$
$$\Updownarrow$$
$$(H_3C)_2N^+H \cdot CH_2 \cdot CH_2 \cdot OH + H_3C \cdot S \cdot CH_2 \cdot CH_2 \cdot CHNH_2 \cdot COOH$$

Since this discovery several such transmethylation reactions have been found to occur in animal metabolism. Moreover, Challenger has shown that in mold metabolism also methyl transfer often plays an essential role.

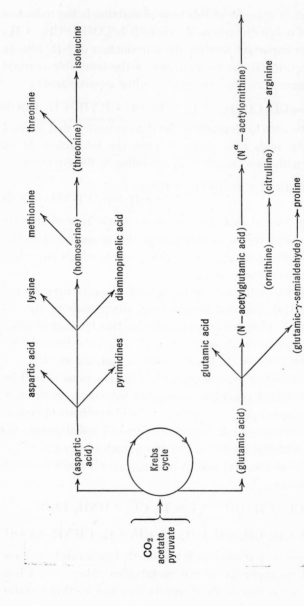

Fig. 17. Pathways of amino acid synthesis in *Escherichia coli*. [From T. H. Abelson *et al*, *Proc. Nat. Acad. Sci. U. S.* 39, 1020 (1953).]

du Vigneaud also drew attention to a process, to which he gave the name transsulfuration, in which a sulfhydryl group is transferred from one organic compound to a second one. The discovery of the way in which this transsulfuration proceeds was the outcome of a study of the biochemical conversion of methionine into cysteine which proved to involve not a decarboxylation of the C_4 compound, but the coöperation of a C_3 compound, serine, in the following manner:

$$HOOC \cdot CHNH_2 \cdot CH_2 \cdot CH_2SH + HOCH_2 \cdot CHNH_2 \cdot COOH \rightarrow$$

homocysteine   serine

$$HOOC \cdot CHNH_2 \cdot CH_2 \cdot CH_2SCH_2 \cdot CHNH_2 \cdot COOH \rightarrow$$

cystathionine

$$HSCH_2 \cdot CHNH_2 \cdot COOH$$

cysteine

Ultimately the result is an exchange between a hydroxyl and a sulfhydryl group.

Summarizing this brief survey of both dissimilatory and assimilatory metabolism, the conclusion seems warranted that the study of microbial metabolism has greatly contributed to the view that, quite independently of the kind of organisms involved, the whole of biochemistry can be reduced to chains of elementary reactions belonging to a small number of types. As such we have met with transhydrogenation, transphosphorylation, transamination, transsulfuration, transacetylation, and transmethylation, in which H, H_2PO_4-, NH_2-, $SH-$, CH_3CO- and CH_3- groups are transferred from one molecule to a second one.

It seems to me that this result, revealing a most edifying unity in the chemical manifestations of life, is another most valuable present that the microbe offers to the "macrobiologist."

The unraveling of the mechanisms whereby the living cell accomplishes the breakdown of substrate molecules and the synthesis of its major cell components has led to some considerations of a more theoretical nature which I wish to take up next. The starting point of my discussion has been a primary division of the metabolic field into two clear-cut parts, aptly designated as dissimilation and assimilation. If we consider the simple case of some aerobic microorganism growing in a medium that contains, besides some inorganic salts, glucose as the sole organic component, such a separation suggests itself. For analysis shows that glucose disappears, and that its carbon is recovered partly in the carbon dioxide formed by slow combustion, partly in the organic constituents of the new cell material formed during growth of the inoculum. This strongly suggests that part of the glucose molecules were completely oxidized to carbon dioxide and water, while concomitantly others were used in synthetic processes.

The complications introduced by the simultaneous occurrence of both dissimilatory and assimilatory events led to the fully comprehensible desire to study the former divorced from the latter. At first sight this does not seem to offer any difficulty; in principle it should be possible to study the respiration of some suitable substrate by a preformed cell population under conditions excluding growth, for instance by eliminating an external nitrogen source. This principle seems to be embodied in the so-called "resting-cell" experiments which, linked with manometric measurements, have found such wide application.

However, we owe to Barker [18] the remarkable discovery that even under these conditions assimilatory processes are far from eliminated. It is true that the lack of nitrogen prevents a harmonious production of all cell constituents necessary for cell multiplication, but all the same it appears that part of the nitrogen-free substrate consumed has escaped the dissimilatory conversion, and has been incorporated into the cells.

This conclusion was based on indirect evidence. In Barker's experiments only such small quantities of the substrate were added to the cell suspension that they were exhausted within the duration of the experiment. By using cells with a low endogenous respiration it became possible to fix rather accurately the moment at which the substrate had been consumed. This enabled Barker to compute the amount of oxygen consumed and of carbon dioxide produced in the conversion of a known quantity of substrate, and it was found that in all cases these figures differed very considerably from the theoretical values based on the assumption of complete combustion. In addition, Barker could show that independently of the nature of the substrate the composition of the products of the assimilatory process always approached the value for CH_2O.

Barker's observations on the colorless alga *Prototheca zopfii* were soon completely confirmed by Giesberger [19] for quite different organisms, namely, various species of the bacterial genus *Spirillum*. Table 10 shows the over-all equations of the conversions of some substrates by *Spirillum serpens*.

TABLE 10. THE OXIDATION OF ORGANIC COMPOUNDS BY *Spirillum serpens* (after Giesberger).

acetic acid	$C_2H_4O_2 + O_2 \rightarrow CO_2 + (CH_2O) + H_2O$
propionic acid	$2C_3H_6O_2 + 6O_2 \rightarrow 5CO_2 + (CH_2O) + 5H_2O$
n butyric acid	$2C_4H_8O_2 + 5O_2 \rightarrow 3CO_2 + 5(CH_2O) + 3H_2O$
lactic acid	$C_3H_6O_3 + 2O_2 \rightarrow 2CO_2 + (CH_2O) + 2H_2O$
pyruvic acid	$2C_3H_4O_3 + 3O_2 \rightarrow 4CO_2 + 2(CH_2O) + 2H_2O$
succinic acid	$2C_4H_6O_4 + 5O_2 \rightarrow 6CO_2 + 2(CH_2O) + 4H_2O$

These results seem to open the way for some far-reaching conclusions. In certain cases there appeared to be a very simple stoichiometric relation between the products of respiration and the assimilatory product (CH_2O). This held, for example, in experiments of both Barker and Giesberger in which acetate was used as a substrate. Here the results answered quite satisfactorily to the equation

$$CH_3 \cdot COOH + O_2 \rightarrow CO_2 + (CH_2O) + H_2O.$$

A critical evaluation of this equation makes it tempting to suggest that in this process we are dealing with an oxygen-consuming conversion of the substrate into one or more cell constituents, and that carbon dioxide and water are mere by-products of this conversion. This would imply that having started the experiment expecting to study a respiration process devoid of assimilatory complications, we have in fact studied an assimilatory process yielding carbon dioxide and water as metabolic "chips." In other words, we should have to conclude that in this case respiration as such does not exist.

Is it possible to generalize this point of view?

In this respect it should be remarked in the first place that the empirical equations established by Barker and by Giesberger were not always of such a simple nature as in the case of acetate. For *Spirillum serpens* oxidizing butyrate Giesberger arrived at the same equation that Barker had found for *Prototheca zopfii*:

$$2C_4H_8O_2 + 5O_2 \rightarrow 3CO_2 + 5(CH_2O) + 3H_2O.$$

Evidently, as also holds for the oxidation of acetate discussed above, it is quite possible to save respiration as an independent process by assuming that in the equation we are in reality dealing with the resultant of two independent processes, one purely dissimilatory and one leading to the formation of assimilatory products. In its most extreme form this could be done as follows:

I $3C_4H_8O_2 + 15O_2 \rightarrow 12CO_2 + 12H_2O$
II $5C_4H_8O_2 + 5O_2 \rightarrow 20(CH_2O)$

or
$$\frac{8C_4H_8O_2 + 20O_2 \rightarrow 12CO_2 + 20(CH_2O) + 12H_2O}{2C_4H_8O_2 + 5O_2 \rightarrow 3CO_2 + 5(CH_2O) + 3H_2O.}$$

It is evident that such a clear-cut separation is unacceptable, since we have already seen that the chain of reactions leading from the substrate to the various cell constituents proceeds with carbon dioxide production, and also includes oxygen-demanding dehydrogenations.

It is, therefore, certain that not all the oxygen consumed and the carbon dioxide produced belong to a separate respiration process. Where the boundary runs cannot be definitely decided, and the temptation remains to consider all the carbon dioxide and water produced as "chips" of the assimilatory processes.

In 1937 when we were first confronted with this idea there was considerable hesitation about accepting it. For at that time Clifton [20] in my laboratory made a remarkable observation in studying the influence of various metabolic inhibitors on the conversions brought about by resting cells of *Pseudomonas calcoacetica* when in contact with nitrogen-free substrates. Clifton found that with a suitable concentration of compounds like sodium azide and 2,4-dinitrophenol it was possible to suppress completely all assimilatory processes, leaving the respiration intact, and even bringing it to completion.

In the case of butyrate this was also manifested in the respiratory quotient which changed from 0.68, according to the equation

$$2C_4H_8O_2 + 7O_2 \rightarrow 5CO_2 + 3(CH_2O) + 5H_2O,$$

to the value 0.80, as required by the equation for complete combustion:

$$C_4H_8O_2 + 5O_2 \rightarrow 4CO_2 + 4H_2O.$$

Apart from throwing a clear light on the mechanism of nitrophenols as effective, though dangerous, "slimming agents," Clifton's observations seemed at that time to indicate that he had succeeded in specifically blocking assimilatory metabolism, without affecting respiration, thus rehabilitating this process in its function of a fully independent energy-yielding process.

In the light of our present-day knowledge of the chemistry of assimilatory processes there are, however, reasons to reject this interpretation as too simple. The idea that dissimilation not only satisfies the energetic needs of assimilation, but that these processes also have material links, and more specifically that dissimilatory intermediates act as starting materials for typical assimilatory reactions, had already been postulated long ago, but convincing proof for this view was lacking. Nowadays there is ample evidence for the view that the formation of cell constituents must be seen as a normal continuation of the chain of reactions that we are used to designating as dissimilation or substrate breakdown. To illustrate this statement with an example, one could say that there is no difference in principle between the pathway that in yeast leads from pyruvic acid to a typical dissimilatory product like ethanol, and the pathway that leads to a typical assimilatory product like stearic acid.

The effect observed by Clifton can be explained by assuming that a particular intermediate metabolic product at a crossroads must find one way specifically blocked, and then proceeds along the other. Spiegelman, Loomis, and others have satisfactorily proved that compounds like dinitrophenol, azide, aureomycin, etc., act by specifically inhibiting the formation of the energy-rich phosphate compounds that occupy such a prominent position in most assimilatory processes.

In this light the respiration process that Clifton proved to proceed in the presence of one of the inhibiting agents must evidently be seen as an artifact, a mental abstraction artificially made true! This also seems to imply that we must consider the tricarboxylic acid cycle to be an instrument of assimilatory metabolism in which the oxygen plays the essential role of making the wheel of life turn by supplying pyridine nucleotides in the oxidized state, indispensable for the successive dehydrogenations leading to the formation of the building stones for assimilation. But it is only when the assimilatory pathways are blocked, and the wheel is "idling," that we come to a conversion of the substrate which can appropriately be designated as respiration. In passing it may be remarked that the phenomena of aging may well be connected with blocks in the assimilatory pathways which naturally develop in the course of time.

Our general conclusion can only be that a separation of dissimilatory and assimilatory processes, so indispensable for a preliminary ordering of the apparent chaos of biochemistry, lacks theoretical justification. In reality both types of processes are closely intermingled; both are only manifestations of biochemistry one and indivisible.

Here we are reminded of the words of Goethe, the philosopher: "Dich im Unendlichen zu finden, muss trennen erst und dann verbinden," which I may perhaps translate thus: "In order to attain infinity, one must separate first, and unify afterwards."

It seems to me that the microbe has again greatly contributed to the recognition of the unitary character of metabolism and that we may see this as a general principle applying to all manifestations of life.

Let us now cast a final look at this unitary biochemistry. The statement appears justified that among the numerous elementary reactions which together constitute biochemistry the transhydrogenations hold a predominant position. In these transhydrogenations hydrogen may be transferred from one molecule to another, or from one part of a molecule to another part; these transhydrogenations may be accompanied by a splitting of a molecule, or by its opposite, a condensation of two molecules.

In summary all these events can be represented by the equations:

$$AH + B \rightarrow A + BH,$$
$$AHB \rightarrow ABH,$$
$$AHB \rightarrow A + BH,$$
$$AH + B \rightarrow ABH.$$

In pondering the question how hydrogen atoms are transferred from one position to another, it is at once clear that the mere acceptance of the coöperation of a coenzyme does not contribute to our insight. For we have already seen that such a coenzyme just adds one new term to the chain of reactions. The riddle remains how a hydrogen-transferring catalyst manages to accept a hydrogen atom from the hydrogen donor preceding it in the chain. The problem is complicated by the fact that the hydrogen-transferring catalysts react only if they are bound to some large protein molecule. It further seems excluded that these protein molecules loaded with their prosthetic groups move freely in the reaction medium; on the contrary, we must conclude that these complexes are just part of some structural unit of the cell. This makes it difficult to imagine that there can be close contact between the various prosthetic groups which consecutively act first as hydrogen acceptors, and then as donors, in a series of hydrogen-transfer reactions, unless the prosthetic groups themselves are assumed to shuttle freely between different proteins. Even this assumption does not provide for a direct contact mechanism in those cases where the reactive part of a prosthetic group is firmly embedded in a protein matrix, a situation which applies, for example, to the iron atom of the cytochromes, according to the studies of Theorell. Nevertheless, this group of substances is considered to play a major role in the final phase of the respiratory chain. It is precisely this situation, however, that opens up prospects for a different interpretation. For here we see a clear demonstration that it is not the transfer of the hydrogen atom which is the essential feature of the coupled dehydrogenation and hydrogenation, but the transfer of an electron which in the cytochromes brings about the change of the iron atom from the trivalent to the bivalent state. This strongly suggests that the same mechanism may be operative also in those cases in which a hydrogen atom is incorporated in the reduced molecule, for we must realize that a transfer of an electron derived from a hydrogen atom results in the formation of a proton or hydrogen ion, and that at any moment an electron entering a molecule can reconstitute a hydrogen atom by the addition of a hydrogen ion from the medium. The realization that in essence hydrogen transfer is nothing but an electron transfer may also explain the reaction between two successive prosthetic groups attached to two different structurally fixed protein molecules. The following considerations do not seem to be invalidated by the convincing experimental proof given by Westheimer, Fisher, Conn, and Vennesland [21] for a direct transfer of a hydrogen atom from substrates to the coenzyme (DPN) of their dehydrogenases.

In this connection it has been emphasized in recent years that the modern ideas regarding the configuration of protein molecules, as shown in Fig. 18, offer the opportunity to imagine how a shift of an electric charge through the hydrogen bridges present between the peptide chains may occur. Both Schmitt and Geissman have developed schemes that show how an electron derived from a substrate molecule may react with an amide group in one of the extreme resonance positions of such a hydrogen-bridged chain, thus causing an electron shift throughout the chain, and finally leading to the expulsion of an electron at the end of the chain and its transfer to some acceptor. Such a scheme, derived

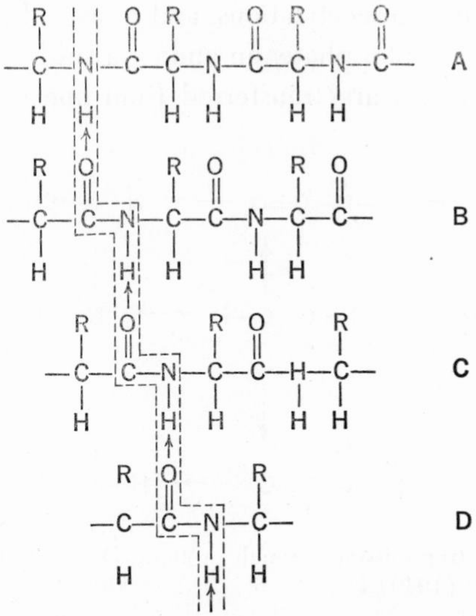

Fig. 18. The role of the protein in electron transmission; A, B, C, and D may be (a) parts of the same protein "backbone" which is folded back and forth upon itself, or (b) parts of separate polypeptide chains that form parts of separate "backbones." [After Huggins from T. Geissman, *Quart. Rev. Biol.* 24, 309, (1949).]

from Geissman's publication,[22] for the case of cytochrome reduction is given in Fig. 19.

Once such a mechanism is accepted there is obviously no difficulty in accepting also an electron transfer from one protein molecule to an adjoining one, since the structural binding between the two may well involve hydrogen bridges. In this way an electron released from one reduced prosthetic group could cause the reduction of the prosthetic group attached to the second protein. This may manifest itself either in a reduction of the valency of some metal or—with the coöperation of a hydrogen ion—in the incorporation of a hydrogen atom in some compound acting as acceptor.

The other types of elementary reactions encountered in our analysis of metabolic processes are amenable to an analogous simplification. Although transphosphorylations, transaminations, transsulfurations, transacetylations, and transmethylations are reactions in which a phosphate, an amino, a sulfhydryl, an acetyl, and a methyl group are transferred from one molecule to an-

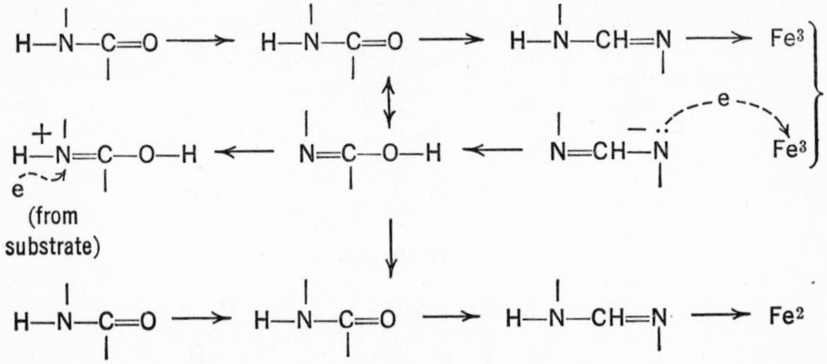

Fig. 19. Electron transmission through proteins. [From T. Geissman, *Quart. Rev. Biol.* **24**, 309 (1949).]

other, it may be argued that the fundamental mechanism whereby this is achieved involves a primary transfer of a charge along a hydrogen-bridged peptide chain of the functional enzymatic protein. As illustrated in Fig. 20 one can imagine that in the case of transacetylation—and the same holds for transphosphorylation—the transfer causes the stabilization in a mesomeric state of the molecule that acts as the donor of the group to be transferred. The ensuing polarization of the molecule enables it to react with an acceptor molecule liable to ionization. One of the ions enters into combination with the oppositely charged pole of the donor molecule. Then the initially formed complex splits, yielding the acceptor combined with the group to be transferred, while the rest of the molecule combines with the second ion of the acceptor.

For transsulfuration, transamination, and transmethylation an analogous mechanism can be visualized, except that here the enzyme brings about an electronic dislocation leading to a negative, instead of a positive, charge of the donor molecule. Thus we are led to the conclusion that the most fundamental character of

General reaction:

$$A\text{—}COCH_3 + BH \rightleftharpoons AH + B\text{—}COCH_3$$

Example:

$$H_2PO_4\text{—}COCH_3 + CoASH \rightleftharpoons H_3PO_4 + CoAS\text{—}COCH_3$$

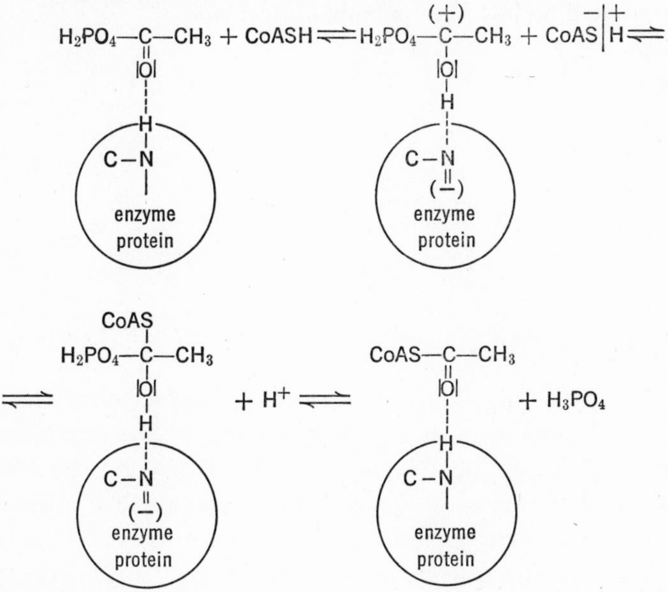

Fig. 20. Scheme for the mechanism of transacetylation. Transphosphorylation proceeds in an analogous way.

the living state is the occurrence in the parts of the cell of a continuous and directed movement of electrons. In transhydrogenations this implies an electron flow from substrate to acceptor; in the other cases this movement is confined to an alternating electron shift in the catalysts involved.

Such reflections suggest the possibility of gradually achieving an even greater simplification and unification of our views on the mechanism of metabolism than can be presently envisaged.

In concluding I should like to give my opinion that, mainly owing to its impressive metabolic diversity, the microbe has made a major contribution to our general insight into the essence of metabolism. There can be no doubt that studies on microbial metabolism have directly fertilized similar studies on animal metabolism in many ways. The next chapter will show that our insight into the metabolism of the photosynthetic green plants has profited no less from microbiological studies.

3

Phototrophic bacteria; key to the understanding of green-plant photosynthesis

C. B. VAN NIEL

It could easily be argued that the very discovery of photosynthesis is closely associated with the activity of microorganisms, in this case with the ability of unicellular green algae to produce oxygen in light. For it was they that produced the gas bubbles in the containers with greenish water that provided Priestley with the first sample of this gas. Priestley's experiments subsequently led to the overthrow of the phlogiston theory, to Jan Ingen-Housz's discoveries, and to the establishment, 150 years ago, of the over-all equation for photosynthesis by de Saussure: [1]

$$CO_2 + H_2O \xrightarrow{\text{light}} \text{Organic matter} + O_2.$$

But Priestley did not know that he had thus been aided by microbes. In fact, the first deliberate use of microorganisms for the study of photosynthesis was not made until a century later. Around 1880 Engelmann hit upon the ingenious idea of employing certain bacteria as sensitive reagents for oxygen. Taking advantage of their ability to remain motile and to accumulate in regions of high oxygen tension, Engelmann demonstrated two important features: (1) the direct connection between oxygen evolution and chloroplasts, already foreshadowed by Ingen-Housz's finding that only the green parts of plants carry out photosynthesis, and (2) the relation between photosynthesis and light absorption by plant pigments.

The first demonstration was accomplished by embedding *Spirogyra* filaments, with their spirally arranged chloroplasts, together

73

with the appropriate "indicator bacteria" in a closed chamber in the absence of air. After a period of illumination the motile bacteria were found to have distributed themselves around the algal filaments in a pattern closely following the twists of the green band.

The second appeared from similar experiments in which a mixture of filamentous green algae and motile bacteria was exposed to a microspectrum. Here the bacteria formed aggregates in regions corresponding to those of maximum light absorption by the green pigment. In similar tests with blue-green, red, and brown algae, Engelmann noticed bacterial swarms also in regions where the blue, brown, and red pigments rather than the chlorophyll are largely responsible for light absorption. From these results he concluded that not only light absorbed by chlorophyll, but also light absorbed by other pigments, can be used effectively for photosynthesis—a conclusion not generally accepted until some sixty years later.

Another notable advance was made by Engelmann's studies on the behavior of motile algae in light of different wavelengths and intensities. Such algae display photokinetic movements which result in their eventual accumulation in regions of optimal light intensity, that is, of maximum absorption by the pigments. And when, in 1883, Engelmann found that certain red-colored bacteria also aggregate in a spectrum in accord with their absorption characteristics, he did not hesitate to infer that these microorganisms must be photosynthetic. This led to the startling conclusion that they can accomplish photosynthesis in the near-infrared region (around 900 mμ).

There is a fifth group of microbes, the luminous bacteria, which has contributed its share, too. Beijerinck, having convincingly shown the strict dependence of bacterial luminescence on the presence of oxygen, introduced the "luminous-bacteria method" as an even more sensitive, and far more specific, test for oxygen than Engelmann's "motile-bacteria method."

Beijerinck furthermore developed the first rational culture

media for the cultivation of microscopic algae. After ascertaining that such media, solidified with gelatin, caused these organisms to grow as spatially separated colonies, Beijerinck successfully applied Koch's principle for their isolation in pure culture. Thus there became available biological material that could be grown under strictly controlled conditions. The great advantages of the unicellular algae for detailed studies of the kinetic aspects of photosynthesis were exploited by Warburg around 1920. With the aid of manometric techniques he established the general characteristics of the light and dark reactions, discovered the photochemical nitrate reduction, and determined the first quantum numbers. Since then algal cultures have become more and more prominent in photosynthesis research, and it is at least doubtful whether progress in this field would have been as great if cultures of *Chlorella, Scenedesmus, Euglena, Chroococcus, Nitzschia*, etc., had not been accessible.

Impressive as may be the above-enumerated contributions of various microorganisms to studies on the photosynthetic process, there is yet another one whose significance can hardly be overestimated. This is Winogradsky's discovery of the chemosynthetic mode of life. It was initiated by his studies on the "sulfur bacteria," a group of organisms whose natural habitat is an H_2S-containing environment, such as a sulfur spring. Winogradsky first established that these microbes require an inorganic oxidizable sulfur compound for growth, which they oxidize to sulfate. From these experiments he inferred that the biologically unusual oxidation provides the bacteria with a source of (chemical) energy. It was further deduced that by virtue of this special energy source the trace amounts of organic substances present in the natural environment could be used exclusively for the synthesis of cell materials.

Somewhat later this interpretation was modified and gave place to an even broader concept, culminating in the theory, launched by Winogradsky in 1890, that the chemical energy obtainable from the oxidation of inorganic substances can be used by certain specialized microorganisms for the assimilation of CO_2, just as in photosynthesis the absorbed radiant energy permits the conversion of CO_2 into organic compounds. This revolutionary extension of the idea that chemical energy derived from the biological oxidation of inorganic substrates can be of significance to the causative organisms was based on Winogradsky's demonstration that pure cultures of nitrifying bacteria, which he was the first to isolate, can multiply in strictly inorganic media provided CO_2 is also present. The existence of yet other kinds of chemosynthetic microorganisms was later established by the studies of Beijerinck, Nathansohn, Jacobsen, Lieske, Waksman, and Starkey with the small sulfur-oxidizing bacteria of the *Thiobacillus* group, and by those of Kaserer, Lebedeff, Niklewski, Grohmann, and Ruhland with the hydrogen-oxidizing bacteria.[2]

The important aspect of this phase of Winogradsky's work is that it showed unequivocally the occurrence of CO_2 assimilation unaided by the absorption of radiant energy. Thus it might have suggested that in photosynthesis also organic matter could be formed from CO_2 through reactions analogous to those operating in chemosynthesis. In that event CO_2 would not be directly involved in the photochemical reaction of the photosynthetic mechanism. Lebedeff seems to have perceived this implication when, in 1908, he wrote that "there appears to be no difference in principle between the mechanism of CO_2 assimilation by green plants and by the chemosynthetic bacteria."[3] But the time was not yet ripe for more detailed speculations and experiments, and Lebedeff's argument was virtually neglected by the students of photosynthesis.

Meanwhile, Winogradsky's interpretation of the metabolism of the sulfur bacteria cast considerable doubt on Engelmann's inference that his photokinetic red bacteria, which are typical sulfur bacteria, are indeed photosynthetic. And when, with the aid of Beijerinck's sensitive and specific luminous-bacteria method, Molisch in 1907, and others since, failed to detect O_2 production by illuminated suspensions of the photokinetic red bacteria, their photosynthetic ability seemed all but refuted.

Nevertheless, there remained some indications that Engelmann had been right. The most significant of these was the ecological argument that the red sulfur bacteria develop in nature only where both H_2S and light are available, and that in laboratory cultures also light exerts a striking influence on their growth. This situation led Buder, in 1919, to the conclusion that both Engelmann and Winogradsky had been right, and that the red sulfur bacteria are photosynthetic as well as chemosynthetic, requiring both light and sulfide.

That Buder's synthesis was sound appeared from the results of the author's experiments with pure cultures of representatives of the group. These convincingly demonstrated the following facts:

1. The red sulfur bacteria can grow in strictly mineral media, with CO_2 as the sole carbon source, but only when the cultures are properly illuminated. This established the need of radiant energy for CO_2 assimilation, or, in other words, the photosynthetic aspect of the metabolism of the organisms.

2. They depend on a supply of H_2S which is oxidized via sulfur to sulfate, and the amount of growth is strictly proportional to the quantity of H_2S available.

Now Buder's interpretation could, in a manner, be used to account for the fact that light is needed for H_2S oxidation because the red sulfur bacteria live in oxygen-free environments. Their presumed photosynthetic activity could, however, supply them with the oxygen required for the oxidation of the sulfur compounds. But this interpretation does not explain why a photosynthetic oxygen production with concomitant CO_2 assimilation cannot be observed after the supply of H_2S and sulfur has been exhausted through oxidation to sulfate. This argument clearly shows that the fundamental problem of accounting for the need of both H_2S and light remained to be resolved. The essential ingredients for a coherent explanation were provided by the clarification brought about in biochemical thinking through the concept of "unity in biochemistry," launched by Kluyver and Donker in 1926 on the basis of an extensive survey of the chemical activities of microorganisms. It implied that all biochemical events can be considered as composed of series of simple step reactions, each of which represents, as documented in Chapter 1, a special case of hydrogen transfer as expressed in the equation for the "master reaction": $AH_2 + B \rightarrow A + BH_2$. Since photosynthesis is undeniably a biochemical process, it could a priori be anticipated that it, too, might accordingly be formulated as a characteristic manifestation of hydrogen-transfer reactions.

The results of quantitative experiments with the red sulfur bacteria can be conveniently expressed by simple, though only approximate, chemical equations. For young cultures, in which the available H_2S has been principally oxidized to intercellularly deposited sulfur, the equation takes the form:

$$2H_2S + CO_2 \xrightarrow{\text{light}} 2S + H_2O + (CH_2O);$$

for old cultures, in which the sulfur has been further oxidized, it becomes:

$$H_2S + 2H_2O + 2CO_2 \xrightarrow{\text{light}} H_2SO_4 + 2(CH_2O).$$

It should be mentioned that the CO_2 utilized is actually converted into bacterial cells; the symbol (CH_2O) in the above equations, representing organic matter on the reduction level of carbohydrate, is merely a close approximation used for the sake of simplicity.

These equations show that here, as in all other cases (see Chapter 1), the biochemical events involve the oxidation of one reactant and the reduction of another. Furthermore, comparison with the equation for green-plant photosynthesis reveals that it, too, falls into line, especially if it is written in the form:

$$2H_2O + CO_2 \xrightarrow{\text{light}} O_2 + H_2O + (CH_2O).$$

The striking similarity of the three equations, together with the recognition that the fundamental characteristics of biochemical processes are transhydrogenation reactions, thus logically suggested that the essence of photosynthesis would be a photochemically operated hydrogen-transfer mechanism in which CO_2, the hydrogen acceptor, is reduced to $(CH_2O) + H_2O$, with the simultaneous oxidation of a hydrogen donor, the latter being H_2S or sulfur in the case of the red sulfur bacteria, and H_2O in the case of green plants. A marked specificity of the respective organisms for particular hydrogen donors, a feature frequently encountered in many nonphotosynthetic organisms, could then be invoked to account for the fact that the red sulfur bacteria require H_2S instead of H_2O as reducing agent for CO_2 assimilation.

This interpretation of photosynthesis as a photochemical oxidation-reduction process finds its most general expression in the equation:

$$2H_2A \quad + \quad CO_2 \quad \xrightarrow{\text{light}} \quad 2A \quad + \quad (CH_2O) \quad + \quad H_2O.$$

H-donor   H-acceptor   oxidized H-donor   reduced acceptor

It suggests the possible existence of photosynthetic processes other than those involving H_2S and H_2O as hydrogen donors. Without entering into details, it may here be stated that in the course of the past twenty-five years several examples have been found of bacterial photosyntheses in which different inorganic as well as various organic substances can function as H_2A.

A direct consequence of the above-mentioned general formulation is that the O_2 produced during photosynthesis by green plants must come in its entirety from H_2O, and not in whole or in part from CO_2. This has been confirmed in special experiments with CO_2 and H_2O, differentially labeled with oxygen isotopes, by Ruben and collaborators and by Winogradow and Teiss. It has also been established with isolated chloroplasts which, as Hill had demonstrated, can still produce O_2 in light although they lack the ability to assimilate CO_2. Because of this failure of chloroplasts to use CO_2 as hydrogen acceptor, O_2 production in this case depends upon the presence of an alternate reducible compound.

The photochemical activities of these structures can thus be represented by the general equation:

$$2H_2O + 2\text{"B"} \xrightarrow{\text{light}} O_2 + 2\text{"BH}_2\text{."}$$

In his early experiments Hill supplied ferric oxalate as the reducible substance. An even more convincing verification of the above equation was provided by the experiments of Warburg and Lüttgens in which quinone was used for this purpose; it yielded hydroquinone, along with the theoretically required amount of O_2, under conditions such that only H_2O could be the source of the evolved gas.

Thus the bacterial photosyntheses, with their dependence on external hydrogen donors other than H_2O and their failure to produce O_2, led to a broadened concept of the photosynthetic process. Obviously the interpretation here presented is no more than a first step toward a better comprehension of its mechanism. Nevertheless, the shift in emphasis resulting from the recognition that its essential feature is an oxidation-reduction reaction in which CO_2, as H-acceptor, becomes transformed into organic matter has made for a more rational approach to problems of detail.

An account of the tortuous route and successive modifications that have led to the gradual development of a somewhat more elaborate and satisfactory picture would be too long; it will suffice to present the current views concerning the main features of the photosynthetic process in the form of a diagram (Fig. 21); a more detailed discussion can be found elsewhere.[4] This diagram expresses the idea that the fundamental photochemical reaction in which the absorbed radiant energy, or the excited pigment molecule, takes part results in a separation of the elements of water. One of the characteristics of the photosynthetic process is that over a certain range its rate is linearly proportional to the light intensity. At present this can best be interpreted by postulating that each absorbed quantum causes the same reaction, involving one H_2O molecule. Since the energy of the quanta with which photosynthesis works is too small (30–45,000 calories per mole quantum) to permit the formation of radicals, it is simplest to invoke the mediation of enzymes which reduce the activation energy of the H_2O molecule and lead to the formation of the entities $E'H$ and $E''OH$.

It is not yet possible to decide whether E' and E'' should be considered as distinct and separate molecular species or as differ-

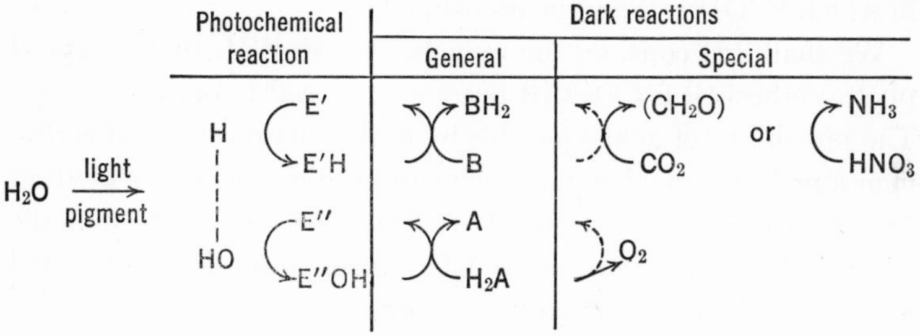

Fig. 21. Scheme of the light and dark reactions in photosynthesis.

ent parts of one and the same molecule. The latter is perhaps easier to envisage. But the application of modern concepts regarding the mechanism of atom and group transfer as a result of electron shifts in large molecules, discussed at the end of Chapter 2, tends to make the distinction largely a matter of semantics as long as the chemical nature of the E' and E'' entities has not been established. The important point to remember is that an electron shift can readily cause a reduction at one extremity and a simultaneous oxidation at another extremity of, for example, a protein molecule with one or more attached coenzymes. In fact, Levitt [5] has recently advanced the intriguing hypothesis that the photochemical reaction in photosynthesis represents the expulsion of an electron from the Mg atom of an excited chlorophyll molecule. Since this pigment occurs in the photosynthetic apparatus as a protein conjugate, the postulated event would result in just the sort of change that has been discussed above. The negatively charged part of the complex, through addition of an H ion, would thus become E'H; the expelled electron would be supplied by another part of the complex; and this, in turn, would yield the E"OH moiety by addition of an OH ion.

As indicated by the diagram, all other reactions in the photosynthetic process are considered to be "dark reactions," that is, biochemical reactions in which light does not play a role. This applies, therefore, to the reductions in which E'H is involved as a catalytic transhydrogenating agent, as well as to the oxidations in which E"OH is the ultimate oxidant.

We shall first consider the reductions with E'H. In any typical photosynthesis it is CO_2 that becomes reduced to organic matter. The possibility of achieving this by dark reactions was, as earlier mentioned, shown when the chemoautotrophs were discovered. In line with Lebedeff's statement we may thus anticipate that the details of the mechanism of CO_2 assimilation in photo- and chemosynthesis have much in common.

Nobody would be so naïve today as to believe that the assimilation of CO_2 is a "simple" reaction. In keeping with current trends it can be expected to represent a vast number of step reactions and "crossroads" with internal and external factors determining the direction in which the various ingredients interact. That this is so has been shown by the experiments of Calvin et al., Gaffron and Fager, and others, in which photosynthesizing cells were supplied with labeled C^*O_2. It was found that the labeled carbon rapidly appears in a large variety of organic compounds. By limiting the time of exposure to the C^*O_2 to a few seconds, it has been possible to reduce the number of labeled substances formed, and present evidence strongly suggests that the primary reaction in which CO_2 is incorporated represents a reductive carboxylation, with phosphoglyceric acid as the product. The problem of the further transformations of this primary assimilation product has lately been under active and imaginative investigation, especially by Calvin and collaborators.[6] The results point to the occurrence of cyclic mechanisms, involving phosphorylated derivatives of 4-, 5-, 6-, and 7-carbon sugars, and of reactions in which 2-carbon fragments of the general composition of glycolaldehyde are transferred. Figure 22 represents a greatly simplified version of the reactions concerned with the formation of a triose molecule, C_3. The most recent evidence indicates that a common mechanism for CO_2 assimilation involves a reaction in which a molecule of CO_2 is added to a molecule of pentose diphosphate with the formation of 2 molecules of phosphoglyceric acid.[19] It stands to reason that other conversions, similar to those encountered in other organisms, must be invoked to account for the ultimate synthesis of the numerous and diverse cell constituents.

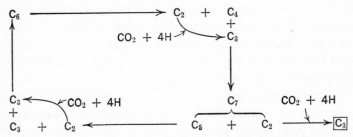

Fig. 22. Reactions of the carbon skeleton during and following photosynthesis.

It should be emphasized that the photosynthetic microorganisms, both algae and bacteria, have played an important role in the studies just discussed.

Assimilation of CO_2 is not the only kind of reduction possible with the aid of E'H. The photochemical nitrate reduction has recently been shown to represent an alternative reaction, and one that can compete with the CO_2 reduction.[7] The most striking demonstration of a "general" reductive mechanism is provided by the Hill reaction. Here an incomplete machine, the chloroplast, can evolve O_2 from H_2O in light provided an external reducible substance, "B," is present. As previously mentioned, this requirement for "B" can be attributed to a deficiency in the enzymatic mechanism operative in various steps by which CO_2 is converted into the normal assimilation products, since E' can function as a catalyst only in the presence of a system that continuously relieves E'H of its hydrogen. Some attempts have been made to complement the machinery of the chloroplasts so that they can use CO_2 as acceptor. Notably successful in this respect have been the studies of Vishniac and Ochoa,[8] who added to chloroplast suspensions enzymes and cofactors known to function in reactions in which CO_2 is activated and incorporated into organic substances. It has thus been possible to achieve, for instance, the formation of O_2 and malate from H_2O, CO_2, and pyruvate by such fortified chloroplast preparations during illumination. From the comparative biochemical viewpoint it is interesting to note that the added enzymes and cofactors had been assembled from a variety of sources, such as pigeon liver, yeast, colibacteria, muscle tissue, etc. This strikingly illustrates Professor Kluyver's remarks about the difficulties of deciding from what organism a functional enzyme mixture is obtained (Chapter 2).

It must, however, be realized that such experiments should not be interpreted to mean that the typical photosynthetic apparatus has thus been reconstructed. In none of the experiments with fortified chloroplast suspensions have products now considered as characteristic stages in normal photosynthesis so far been obtained. It is evident that the results achieved by Calvin *et al.* must serve as a guide for future studies of this kind, and warn us against hasty conclusions. But it should also be obvious that the details of the mechanism of CO_2 assimilation need not be studied exclusively with photosynthetic organisms. In the long run any advance in our understanding of the synthesis of particular substances by any kind of organism is apt to further our understanding of photosynthesis as well.

As an aside it may be remarked that the presumed inability of isolated chloroplasts to assimilate CO_2 has been challenged by the recent report of Arnon, Allen, and Whatley,[9] in which it is shown that chloroplast suspensions, prepared by special methods, can still effect a pronounced CO_2 fixation.

About the nature of E' not much can be said at present. The

work of Vishniac and Ochoa has shown that illuminated chloroplasts can reduce pyridine nucleotides. Whether these universal biocatalysts are directly identifiable with E′, or should be considered as more or less distantly linked to it, remains to be determined. Of great importance in this connection is the recent work of Calvin which seems to implicate lipoic acid as a functional component of the photosynthetic apparatus. This is especially appealing because lipoic acid has been identified as a constituent of enzymes involved in oxidative decarboxylations. Hence its operation in the reverse type of reaction, a reductive carboxylation, seems a far from remote possibility.

Calvin has further postulated that lipoic acid may also be involved directly in the series of events that culminates in the production of O_2. This leads us to a consideration of the reactions in which E″OH takes part. Here we must distinguish two main variants: (1) the reactions occurring in green plants, and there resulting in the evolution of O_2, and (2) the reactions taking place in the photosynthetic bacteria, where the recycling of the E″ enzyme moiety is presumably coupled with the oxidation of various substrates, "H_2A."

As indicated by Fig. 21, we can represent the formation of E″OH as resulting from the photolysis of H_2O. By assigning to this entity a different degree of stability in bacterial and in green-plant photosyntheses the fundamental differences in the characteristics of the two types can be glimpsed. We may assume that E″OH in green plants is sufficiently labile so that it can reconstitute E″ by elimination of O_2, whereas in the bacteria it is a much more stable product, so that photosynthesis, that is, continued photolysis of H_2O, here depends on its continual reduction by an external reductant. The latter should, of course, be envisaged as accomplished through the mediation of the appropriate dehydrogenases and transfer mechanisms.

This concept also accounts for the observation that any and all compounds which can serve as "H_2A" for bacterial photosyntheses can equally well be oxidized by the respective organisms with O_2 in darkness. Thus light and O_2 are equivalent from the point of view of substrate oxidation. However, the oxidant produced during illumination is not O_2 itself, but rather E"OH.

The equivalence of light and O_2 in the metabolism of the photosynthetic bacteria is most clearly demonstrated by the fact that the rate of oxidation of any specific hydrogen donor, H_2A, is identical in the absence of O_2 at a sufficiently high light intensity, and in darkness when O_2 is present. This implies that usually the speed with which the E"–E"OH cycle turns over is the bottleneck determining the rate of bacterial photosyntheses. By using combinations of different oxidizable substances, each requiring different enzymes for their oxidation—such as mixtures of thiosulfate and an organic acid, for example—it can be demonstrated that the rate of photosynthesis under these conditions is the sum of the rates found with the individual substrates singly. The same phenomenon may be observed in comparable experiments carried out in darkness but in the presence of O_2; they show that the different substrates disappear simultaneously, each one at its own pace, and that the rate of O_2 utilization is additive.

This interpretation also shows that one may consider the photosynthetic bacteria as counterparts of Hill's chloroplasts. The latter are deficient in a mechanism for relieving the E'H of its hydrogen; hence they can function continuously only in the presence of an externally added oxidizing agent, "B," whereas the photosynthetic bacteria do not possess a mechanism for the spontaneous regeneration of E" from E"OH, and hence require an external reducing agent, "H_2A."

A further consequence of the present interpretation is that the oxidation of H_2A in photosynthesis may be *merely* a means for recycling E". In that case the energy available from the oxidation would be useless to the metabolism of the organisms. The experiments of Wassink, Katz, and Dorrestein [10] with a red sulfur bacterium, and of Larsen et al.[11] with green sulfur bacteria indicate that this is so. The argument goes as follows. In green-plant photosynthesis only one source of energy is available; this is light.

From the most dependable measurements, obtained in several different laboratories, and by various techniques, it appears that the complete assimilation of one molecule of CO_2 and the production of one molecule of O_2 generally requires the absorption of 8 quanta of radiant energy. This represents a thermodynamic efficiency of about 30 percent. The photosynthetic bacteria can, theoretically, count on two different energy sources: light and chemical energy liberated during the oxidation of H_2A. On the basis of energetic considerations they should, therefore, be able to assimilate more CO_2 per quantum of absorbed radiant energy if the oxidation yielded potentially utilizable energy. But the measurements with hydrogen, thiosulfate, and tetrathionate as H_2A have shown that in all cases about 8 quanta of radiant energy are absorbed per molecule of CO_2 assimilated, giving efficiency values of 0.5, 8.3, and 8.5 percent, respectively. The results obtained with H_2 are the most instructive; theoretically, assimilation at about 30-percent efficiency should require no more than 0.1 quantum per molecule. It thus appears that the oxidation energy released in the bacterial photosyntheses is wasted. This is fully consistent with the interpretation in which the oxidation of H_2A is conceived as the means for making the cycling of E'' possible.

Some remarks about the nature of E'' may be in order. In green-plant photosynthesis the oxidation product, $E''OH$, is responsible for the evolution of O_2. Now, biological O_2 production is so far known only as the result of an enzymatic decomposition of H_2O_2 by catalase. However, this specific reaction cannot be invoked to explain the liberation of O_2 in photosynthesis because Gaffron has shown that normal photosynthesis can occur under conditions of complete catalase inactivity. It is therefore necessary to search for alternative explanations. Reasoning on the basis of comparative biochemical considerations suggests that it may be useful to examine somewhat comparable phenomena for possible clues. In this connection it appears promising to view the photosynthetic O_2 evolution as the reversal of the mechanism involved in the utilization of O_2 for biological oxidations. Even though little is known concerning the details of such reactions, it is generally accepted that an important role is here played by cytochromes. This suggests, therefore, the possibility of a cytochrome-mediated process in photosynthetic O_2 production.[12]

Recently Hill and Davenport [13] have found in chloroplasts from green plants a specific cytochrome, similar to, but not identical with, cytochrome C. Following this lead Elsden in England, and Vernon and Kamen in the United States, have examined photosynthetic bacteria for cytochromes. An important result of these investigations is that it now appears that each type of photosynthetic organism may contain its own specific cytochrome. In view of the physicochemical properties exhibited by the cytochrome obtained from one of the photosynthetic bacteria, Elsden has even suggested that these substances may actually represent the substance indicated in Fig. 21 by E″.[14]

Though it is obviously important to demonstrate that a compound with the requisite properties is present in a particular situation, this is by no means equivalent to establishing that it is functional in the manner postulated. It is, therefore, very significant that Duysens [15] has discovered a phenomenon that strongly supports Elsden's contention. Duysens found that if a suspension of photosynthetic bacteria is irradiated with light absorbed by the green pigment bacteriochlorophyll, the suspension displays an instantaneous change in absorption spectrum. The observed change is identical with that resulting from a conversion of the reduced to the oxidized form of the specific cytochrome component of the organisms. In darkness the reverse happens. We know, therefore, that the cytochrome undergoes changes compatible with those that would be expected if it were E″. It must, however, be admitted that this does not necessarily imply identity of the various cytochromes of the photosynthetic organisms and E″. We should certainly recognize the possibility that eventually the cytochromes may be shown to be only more or less closely linked with another kind of molecule, E″ proper. Special attention may here be called to Calvin's recent ideas on the function of lipoic acid in photosynthesis. From the consideration that the strained disulfide ring renders the molecule particularly suitable to act as both H and OH acceptor, as shown by the equation

$$\text{S——S} + \text{HOH} \rightarrow \underset{\text{H} \quad \text{OH}}{\text{S} \quad \text{S}} ,$$

Calvin has postulated that lipoic acid may function not only as E′, but simultaneously also as E″. It seems reasonable to expect that a further clarification of the situation will soon be achieved.

Photosynthesis proceeds under the influence of radiant energy absorbed by special pigments. As mentioned earlier, Engelmann had concluded from his experiments that the blue-green, brown, and red algae can photosynthesize with light primarily absorbed not by chlorophyll but by the accessory pigments. For many years this idea was considered almost as a heresy, and the notion became prevalent that only light absorbed by chlorophyll was effective in bringing about photosynthesis.

The photosynthetic bacteria also contain chlorophyllous pigments; in the red ones their color is masked by various yellow to purple carotenoids. The results of early experiments on the possible role of these pigments were in line with the ideas developed from studies on algae. Especially the measurements of Roelofsen and of French in the mid-1930's indicated that light absorbed by the carotenoids cannot be used for photosynthesis of the red bacteria.

But since about 1940 our notions have drastically changed. Emerson and Lewis, with microscopic blue-green algae, showed that photosynthesis proceeds fully as effectively in light absorbed by phycocyanin as in light absorbed by chlorophyll. Dutton and Manning, and later Wassink, made similar observations with diatoms. The work of Blinks, Haxo, and Yocum extended these findings to include the accessory pigments of the red and brown algae.[16] Finally, Manten, on the basis of phototaxis studies, developed a good argument for the thesis that carotenoid pigments in photosynthetic bacteria are also photosynthetically effective, and Clayton actually succeeded in growing these organisms in green light where the relative absorption by bacteriochlorophyll is negligible as compared with that by the carotenoids. By appropriate adjustments of the light intensities Clayton even demonstrated identical growth rates in green and infrared light, respectively. The direct measurements of photosynthetic activity of these bacteria in different spectral regions by Thomas *et al.* have established rate maxima corresponding to absorption maxima of a carotenoid.

These indisputable results have led to the question whether photosynthesis under the influence of light absorbed by pigments other than chlorophyll proceeds in a manner not involving chlorophyll at all, or whether energy absorbed by the accessory pigments can be transferred to chlorophyll and thus enable the latter to function as the sole photoactivated participant in the photochemical reaction. Yocum has used two general arguments in favor of the latter view: the evolutionary argument that no photosynthetic organism is known which is devoid of chlorophyll, and the ecological one that photosynthetic organisms with accessory pigments are thereby enabled to occupy special environmental niches where only light absorbed by nonchlorophyllous substances is available.

Attempts to demonstrate energy transfer between different pigments in photosynthetic organisms were first made by Arnold in experiments with blue-green algae. Using light specifically absorbed by the blue accessory pigment, phycocyanin, he observed that the organisms emit light by fluorescence—of chlorophyll! This implied that chlorophyll had become excited, and this with energy initially absorbed by phycocyanin. Arnold and Oppenheimer,[17] in analyzing this situation, concluded that transfer of energy from phycocyanin to chlorophyll should be ascribed to an "internal conversion."

Working along the same lines, but with improved methods which permitted quantitative determinations of the fluorescence yield, Duysens [18] has recently demonstrated that a virtually complete transfer of excitation energy occurs from phycoerythrin to phycocyanin, from the latter to chlorophyll, and from chlorophyll *b* to chlorophyll *a*. Energy transfer from carotenoids to chlorophyll has also been measured; it seems, however, less efficient (20–50 percent, though it is probably higher from fucoxanthin). The mechanism envisaged, and denoted by the term "inductive resonance," is similar to that of "internal conversion"; it requires that the molecules between which the transfer takes place be in very close proximity. Determinations of the pigment concentrations in the chloroplasts and grana have yielded values of the order of 0.1–0.2 *M* or even higher; under the circumstances the proposed mechanism can certainly operate.

It seems, therefore, that only one special type of pigment—chlorophyll *a* in green plants, bacteriochlorophyll in purple bacteria, and chlorobium chlorophyll in the green sulfur bacteria—is intimately involved in the photochemical reaction of the different photosyntheses, but that, through the elaboration of various accessory pigments, the region of the spectrum for effective photosynthesis has been considerably extended. Especially important in this respect are the photosynthetic bacteria with their specific chlorophylls, which exhibit pronounced absorption maxima over almost the entire range from 700 to 900 $m\mu$.

From the foregoing discussion it may be concluded that much progress has been made in our interpretation of the photosynthetic process, and that more may be expected in the near future. It is a pleasure indeed to acknowledge a debt of gratitude to the microorganisms whose peculiarities have contributed so much to our better understanding of its mechanism. It was the possibility of applying Kluyver's principles of comparative biochemistry to photosynthesis that has at long last resulted in removing this process from the position of splendid isolation in which it had for so long remained, and the photosynthetic bacteria with their curious metabolic properties made this feasible. The outcome of the comparative biochemical approach has been the development of fundamental modifications of earlier concepts, and this, in turn, has provided an opportunity for markedly broadening the basis of an experimental attack on the numerous aspects of the problem.

4

Life's flexibility; microbial adaptation

A. J. KLUYVER

The first two chapters on microbial metabolism may have created the impression that each microbial species is characterized by a specific and fixed metabolic pattern. However, such a statement would be a serious underevaluation of life's potencies. On the contrary, it seems to me that the study of the microbe has made another important contribution to biology by throwing a clear light on the flexibility of the living cell with regard to its metabolism. It has been convincingly demonstrated that the enzymatic equipment of the progeny of one cell, and hence its metabolic activity, are liable to profound changes engendered by its previous history. It will at once be evident that this situation is not without implications of a general nature.

In this chapter I shall aim at giving a documentation for the metabolic variability of the microbial cell, and discuss its significance. Before doing so, a few remarks should be made.

In the first place I must observe that a change in environmental conditions which makes a cell acquire a metabolic activity that was lacking in its ancestry is often of such a nature that the new quality adds materially to the well-being of the cell, for example, by enabling it to proliferate in the new environment. In other words, owing to the change in enzymatic equipment the cell better fits its new environment, and under these circumstances there seems to be every reason to use the word "adaptation" for the phenomenon in question. In what follows I shall, therefore, use the words "adapt" and "adaptation" in this wide sense, independent of the causes underlying the change. The remark could not be omitted, because much misunderstanding has been caused by authors who—in my opinion quite arbitrarily— have restricted the meaning of the term "adaptation" to those variations that are not accompanied by a change of the genotype of the cell.

Now that I have used the word adaptation, I have also to confess that the title I have chosen for this chapter is much too broad. It is well known that the microbe world offers many striking examples of adaptation which cannot at first sight be regarded as being due to changes in enzymatic equipment of the cell. I need only mention the adaptation of certain microbes to high temperatures, high salt concentrations, or certain inhibitory drugs. It is clear that all these phenomena are as many testimonials to life's stupendous flexibility. If we ponder the ways in which the progeny of a cell manages to adapt itself to a mode of life under conditions that are definitely adverse to the individual which acted as the starting point of the clone, it is difficult to escape the conclusion that the adapted cell is equipped with catalysts which differ from those present in the mother cell. Hence, it is likely that a deeper penetration into the processes underlying these types of adaptation will show that they too can be ascribed to the formation of enzyme systems which initially were lacking. I shall limit the discussion to those cases of adaptation which clearly find their expression in the appearance of one or more new biocatalysts.

The earlier studies on the dependence of enzyme production on external conditions were made with growing cultures and mainly dealt with the influence of the variation in cultural conditions on the quantity of certain hydrolases excreted into the culture medium. The chief result of these studies is perhaps that the formation of a certain hydrolase is not determined by the presence of the corresponding substrate in the culture medium; in certain cases its presence may be promotive from a quantitative point of view, but exceptions to this rule are not at all rare.

The study of what was then called "enzymatic adaptation" entered a new epoch in 1930, when the Finnish investigator Karström [1] published a systematic investigation on the conditions that determine the production of enzyme systems necessary for the fermentation of different sugars by various bacteria. Karström introduced a new methodological principle in these adaptation studies. He cultivated a bacterial strain in different culture media, and then tested the collected and washed cells for their ability to ferment the various sugars under conditions excluding further proliferation of the cells. This was attained by using test media to which no nitrogen source had been added, while moreover the duration of the test was restricted to one or two hours.

The experiments showed that the cells frequently were able to ferment a certain sugar only if they had been grown in a medium containing this carbohydrate. This held for instance for the fermentation of arabinose, galactose, maltose, and lactose by a strain of *Betacoccus arabinosaceus*. On the other hand the ability to ferment glucose, fructose, and mannose appeared to be independent of the previous history of the cells. This led Karström to the introduction of the term "adaptive" and "constitutive" for the characterization of the enzyme systems responsible for the fermentation in each of the two categories.

The merit of Karström's technique is undoubtedly that it aims at a distinction between the presence of a certain enzyme in a cell population and the potentiality of the cells to produce this enzyme under suitable conditions.

Since 1930 numerous investigations have shown that the conditions under which cells originate materially influence the nature of their enzymatic equipment. Consider first certain results obtained by Perquin [2] in his studies on mold metabolism. It was these investigations which in 1932 led to the introduction of the "shake-culture method" in microbiology.[3] This was a direct consequence of the desirability of distinguishing between the influences of previous history and of actual environmental conditions on the metabolic activity of mold cells. This made it indispensable to procure a uniform cell material, and it needs no explanation that the mycelial mat as obtained in the normal stationary culture does not answer this requirement. After introducing the "shake mycelium" Perquin soon found that, depending on the composition of the medium in which the fungal cells had been grown, there were considerable differences in their metabolic behavior (Table 11). Under identical test conditions one type of mycelium converted glucose almost quantitatively into gluconic acid, while a second type produced only carbon dioxide. Under a different set of test conditions one type of cell produced a considerable quantity of citric acid, others again only carbon dioxide.

Several further examples of the enzymatic variability of the cell can be found in the literature; as a general illustration I may use the following investigations carried out in the Delft laboratory.

As has already been remarked in the first chapter there is a certain group of so-called denitrifying bacteria which can grow at the expense of some organic substrate when air is admitted to the culture, but which are able to thrive equally well under anaerobic conditions provided that nitrate is added to the medium. Under the latter conditions the nitrate obviously acts as a substitute for free oxygen as hydrogen acceptor in dissimilation, and is reduced mainly to nitrogen.

My former collaborator, van Olden,[4] who in 1940 started an investigation on specific inhibitors of the denitrification process, met with unexpected difficulties during manometric experiments with cells of *Micrococcus denitrificans* harvested from an aerobic culture on peptone agar. As can be seen from Fig. 23, no nitrogen was evolved during incubation for as long as five hours, although in an experiment in which oxygen was present the bacteria showed a vigorous respiration. This was the more remarkable because in an anaerobic *growth* experiment the organisms developed rapidly and produced copious amounts of nitrogen. The only possible explanation seemed to be that bacteria grown in the absence of nitrate are entirely devoid of the catalytic system activating the nitrate as hydrogen acceptor, that is, the nitrate reductase or nitratase. To test this possibility the experiments were

TABLE 11. INFLUENCE OF THE COMPOSITION OF THE GROWTH MEDIUM ON THE DISSIMILATORY PROPERTIES OF "RESTING" MYCELIUM OF *Aspergillus niger* (after Perquin).

Gluconic acid formation		
Growth medium	Percentage of glucose converted into	
	gluconic acid	carbon dioxide (+ mycelium)
basic medium I with $NaNO_3$	100	—
basic medium I with $(NH_4)_2SO_4$	—	100

Citric acid formation		
Growth medium	Percentage of saccharose converted into	
	citric acid	carbon dioxide (+ mycelium)
basic medium II with NH_4Cl and $ZnSO_4$ (tr.)	39	61
basic medium II with NH_4NO_3 and KH_2PO_4 (extra)	—	100

repeated with cells harvested from an aerobic culture on peptone agar to which 0.5 percent of nitrate had been added, but the result was disappointing; the cells showed only very slight activity in the anaerobic manometric experiment. It was then decided to

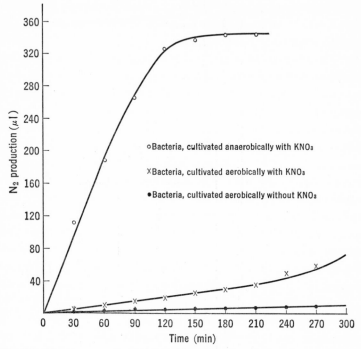

Fig. 23. *Micrococcus denitrificans;* denitrification with sodium acetate as substrate. [From E. van Olden, *Koninkl. Ned. Akad. Wetenschap., Proc.* 53, 635 (1940).]

test bacteria taken in the very act of denitrification, namely, bacteria grown on peptone agar with addition of 2 percent of potassium nitrate, free oxygen being excluded. This time there was also a vigorous nitrate reduction in the manometric experiment, as judged by gas evolution and nitrate consumption. The conclusion must be that the cells of *Micrococcus denitrificans* produce the enzyme nitratase only if the environment in which they grow forces them to renounce their normal energy-yielding process, respiration, and to rely on denitrification. It is clear that we meet here with a typical case of adaptation, and the nitratase is for the bacterium in question an adaptive enzyme in the sense of Karström.

In recent years we have more or less incidentally expanded our observations on the adaptive power of *Micrococcus denitrificans,* and have obtained some results that are perhaps worth considering. The starting point of these investigations, performed by my collaborator Verhoeven and some other workers,[5] was the question whether there exist bacteria that can proliferate at the expense of the simple system molecular hydrogen–nitrate. It had already been shown long ago that in "resting-cell" experiments certain bacterial species can use molecular hydrogen for the reduction of nitrate which then was converted into nitrite or ammonia. But no evidence was available that molecular hydrogen could act as a hydrogen donor in true dissimilatory nitrate reduction, as exemplified in denitrification. It was, therefore, decided to test in manometric experiments five of the more common denitrifying bacterial species — including *Micrococcus denitrificans—* for their ablty to consume hydrogen with nitrate as acceptor. Taking into account van Olden's experiences regarding the adaptive character of the nitratase, the bacteria were grown anaerobically on peptone agar to which 1 percent of nitrate was added. In order to ensure anaerobiosis the cultivation took place in a hydrogen atmosphere, this gas being chosen because a previous study of some *Knallgas* bacteria had taught us that the enzyme activating gaseous hydrogen, hydrogenase, is also a typical adaptive enzyme.

However, the results obtained in these experiments were negative throughout; none of the five species consumed hydrogen, strongly suggesting that, if there exist bacteria that can denitrify with molecular hydrogen, they are a specific type and do not belong to the group of the better-known denitrifying species.

Accordingly, it was decided to start enrichment cultures for bacteria that can grow with molecular hydrogen as sole hydrogen donor in denitrification. To this end the mineral medium devised by Grohmann for hydrogen-oxidizing bacteria was used with the addition of 2 percent of potassium nitrate. The medium was inoculated with garden soil; the gas phase was replaced by hydrogen; and the culture was incubated at 30°C on a continuous shaker. Within 2 or 3 days a considerable reduction of gas pressure could readily be established; ultimately it reached four-fifths of the original value, indicating a total consumption of hydrogen coupled with the production of nitrogen amounting to one-fifth of the volume of hydrogen initially present. However, attempts to isolate the causative bacterium on a mineral-agar medium of the same composition were quite unsuccessful. Moreover, transfers from the enrichment culture into fresh media also quickly lost their activity.

This disappointing result led to the assumption that the bacteria active in the crude culture were not strict autotrophes, but that their proliferation might depend on small quantities of organic matter brought into the enrichment medium with the inoculum. Following this trend of thought, transfers were made into the mineral medium, to which at the same time a small quantity of yeast autolysate was added. The effect was eminently satisfactory; repeated transfers consistently yielded vigorous cultures, and the isolation on a similarly enriched agar medium offered no difficulties. The pure culture likewise grew in the new medium with hydrogen consumption and nitrogen evolution.

Evidently we were dealing here with a chemometatrophic bacterium in the sense of Lwoff. Further investigation showed, however, that it was also quite capable of a heterotrophic mode of life, as manifested by its growth in several media containing some simple organic compound either in the presence of free oxygen or with nitrate in denitrification experiments.

To our great surprise, continued investigation of the properties of the bacterium led to the conclusion that the new isolate was identical with *Micrococcus denitrificans* Beijerinck. At first this conclusion seemed incompatible with the negative behavior of the "resting cells" of the type strain of this species, as reported earlier. It was therefore most gratifying that this type strain—which had been isolated more than forty years before by Beijerinck, and continuously propagated as an aerobic organism on peptone agar—was quite prepared to grow at the expense of the molecular hydrogen–nitrate system in the mineral medium enriched with some drops of yeast autolysate.

Notwithstanding this, the earlier established inability of the "resting cells" of the type strain remained to be explained, especially since the cultivation of these cells on a nitrate-containing peptone agar in a hydrogen atmosphere seemed to guarantee suitable conditions for an adaptive formation of both nitratase and hydrogenase. It was decided to repeat the experiment, simultaneously conducting a parallel experiment with "resting cells" grown in a hydrogen atmosphere on Grohmann's mineral agar to which 1 percent of KNO_3 and a small quantity of yeast autolysate had been added. These experiments led to the remarkable result that the latter cells actively absorbed large amounts of hydrogen, while the bacteria grown on the peptone nitrate medium again were entirely inactive.

Evidently we must conclude from these results that for the production of hydrogenase in *M. denitrificans* not only the presence of hydrogen but also the absence of organic hydrogen donors is required.

In view of the general interchangeability of oxygen and nitrate for denitrifying bacteria it seemed probable that suitably adapted cells of *M. denitrificans* would also be able to catalyze the reaction between molecular hydrogen and molecular oxygen, the so-called *Knallgas* reaction. As is shown in Fig. 24 this assumption proved, indeed, to be correct. It is interesting to note that the hydrogen consumption is practically the same when oxygen and when nitrate act as hydrogen acceptors, indicating that the rates of both reactions are determined by the capacity of the hydrogenase.

It had thus become clear that in *M. denitrificans* we are dealing with an organism endowed with quite amazingly many-sided potencies. Evidently it can satisfy its energy demands from the following systems: organic matter–molecular oxygen, organic matter–nitrate, molecular hydrogen–molecular oxygen, and finally

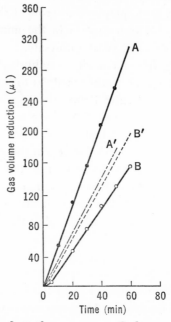

Fig. 24. *Micrococcus denitrificans* grown on Grohmann medium with nitrate and a drop of yeast autolysate in a hydrogen atmosphere. Curve A, gas consumption in 50 percent H_2, 10 percent O_2, and 40 percent N_2 in the absence of nitrate; curve B, gas reduction in hydrogen with nitrate, curves A' and B' give the net hydrogen consumption in the two cases. [From W. Verhoeven *et al.*, *Antonie van Leeuwenhoek. J. Microbiol. Serol. 20*, 282 (1954).]

molecular hydrogen–nitrate. On the other hand, the experiments leave no doubt that a given cell population is able to use only some of these energy sources, the others becoming available only after growth under suitable conditions.

It was, therefore, decided to make a more systematic investigation of the factors controlling the adaptation toward the various hydrogen acceptors and hydrogen donors. The hydrogen acceptor study included, besides oxygen and nitrate, also nitrite and nitrous oxide, which are presumed to be intermediate products of the reduction of nitrate to molecular nitrogen; as hydrogen donor molecular hydrogen and an organic substrate were used.

Figure 25 illustrates the behavior of *M. denitrificans* grown as

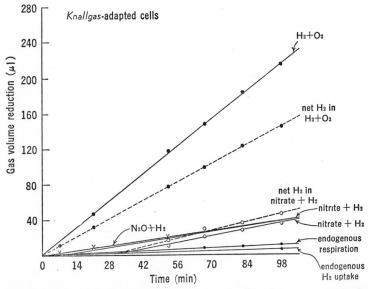

Fig. 25. *Micrococcus denitrificans* grown as a *knallgas* bacterium on Grohmann medium. [From A. J. Kluyver and W. Verhoeven, *Antonie van Leeuwenhoek. J. Microbiol. Serol. 20*, 340 (1954).]

a *Knallgas* bacterium on Grohmann's medium. As might be expected, there is a vigorous hydrogen consumption in the presence of oxygen. But if the oxygen is replaced by either nitrate, nitrite, or nitrous oxide, this consumption is almost negligible, although there appears to be some adaptation to nitrate after a lag period of about 30 minutes. These results obviously mean that nitratase is lacking also in cells grown with molecular hydrogen as donor in the absence of nitrate.

Figure 26 shows that the situation is quite different if we test cells which in their growth phase have been depending on denitrification. This time the cells were grown on a Grohmann medium with nitrate and a small amount of yeast autolysate in an atmosphere of pure hydrogen. They show an active hydrogen

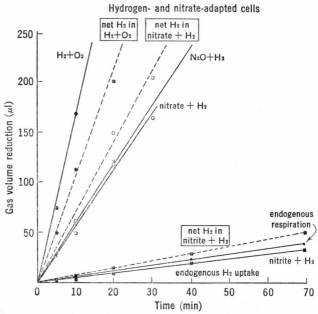

Fig. 26. *Micrococcus denitrificans* grown on Grohmann agar with 1 percent of KNO₃ and a drop of yeast autolysate in a hydrogen atmosphere. [From A. J. Kluyver and W. Verhoeven, *Antonie van Leeuwenhoek. J. Microbiol. Serol. 20,* 341 (1954).]

consumption both with nitrate and with nitrous oxide, as well as with oxygen. Since the bacteria had been grown in the absence of oxygen we must conclude that, in contrast to nitratase, the oxygen-activating catalyst is a constitutive enzyme in the sense of Karström.

Contrary to expectation, nitrite proved to be unsuitable as hydrogen acceptor for hydrogen oxidation. Growth on nitrite-containing agar plates in a hydrogen atmosphere was scanty,

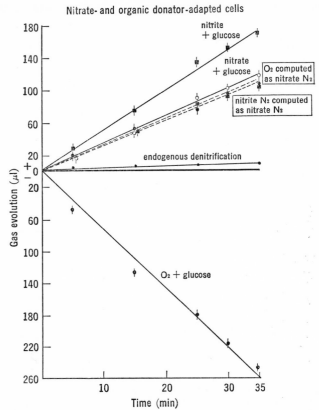

Fig. 27. *Micrococcus denitrificans* grown on peptone agar, 1 percent KNO₃, 1 percent glucose, in a nitrogen atmosphere. [From A. J. Kluyver and W. Verhoeven, *Antonie van Leeuwenhoek. J. Microbiol. Serol. 20*, 349 (1954).]

while resting cells of any origin were unable to reduce nitrite with molecular hydrogen.

This anomalous behavior may be attributed to a specific inhibitory action of nitrite on the hydrogenase. As shown by Fig. 27, nitrite is a perfectly suitable acceptor when an organic substrate is used as hydrogen donor. Since, furthermore, the rate of nitrogen evolution from nitrate is almost exactly three-fifths of that from nitrite, it is clear that the nitrite-reducing enzyme is not

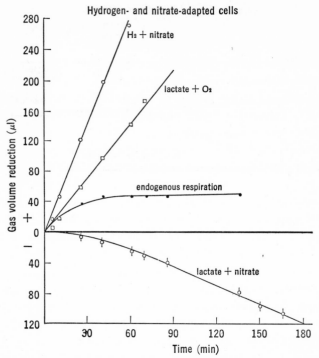

Fig. 28. *Micrococcus denitrificans* grown on Grohmann agar with 1 percent KNO$_3$ and a drop of yeast autolysate in a hydrogen atmosphere. [From A. J. Kluyver and W. Verhoeven, *Antonie van Leeuwenhoek. J. Microbiol. Serol.* 20, 354 (1954).]

limiting, and that the rate of both processes is again determined by the capacity of the dehydrogenase.

As for the adaptability of *M. denitrificans* toward the hydrogen donors, it was found, in agreement with earlier observations, that bacteria grown on peptone agar with 1 percent of glucose and 1 percent of nitrate in a hydrogen atmosphere are perfectly able to dehydrogenate lactate both with oxygen and with nitrate as acceptor, but cannot catalyze the reactions between molecular hydrogen and these acceptors.

The results presented in Fig. 28 refer to bacteria adapted to both hydrogen and nitrate. Naturally they consume hydrogen ac-

tively in the presence of nitrate. Noteworthy, however, is the behavior of these "autotrophically" grown bacteria toward an organic hydrogen donor such as lactate. While in the respiration
experiment the lactate dehydrogenation proceeds at a satisfactory
rate without any noticeable adaptation, the bacteria do not seem
to be equipped to use lactate as a hydrogen donor in the denitrification experiment. Only after a considerable lag period does
an adaptation become manifest, but in the course of the experiment the denitrification rate remains low. Apparently the production of lactate dehydrogenase proceeds rapidly under aerobic, but
only tardily under anaerobic, conditions.

Summarizing the foregoing, it seems warranted to conclude
that *M. denitrificans* offers a striking example of life's flexibility. It
can live as a heterotrophe, depending on the oxidation of some
organic substrate, not only with free oxygen, but also with nitrate
as a substitute for the latter; next it turns out to be a fully autotrophic organism able to thrive on the *Knallgas* system; and finally
it emerges as a chemometatrophic organism displaying the seemingly exceptional quality of thriving on the system molecular hydrogen–nitrate. But it has been clearly shown that the ability to
use hydrogen as donor and nitrate as acceptor depends on the
presence of special enzymes which are produced only in response
to well-defined conditions during growth.

How strongly the potentiality to produce these enzymes is fixed
in the genetic apparatus of the organism is demonstrated in a
most convincing way by the behavior of Beijerinck's original culture, which, maintained for forty years—that is, for thousands of
generations—on peptone agar, on being transferred to an environment where molecular hydrogen is the only energy source available, answers nature's challenge by the brave device: "Here I
am, I can also act differently!"

I have dwelt at some length on the special case of *Micrococcus
denitrificans* because it seemed to me that this might be an effective way of impressing upon the reader the marvel of the char-

acteristic of life that is embodied in the word flexibility. I shall now attempt to give a survey of what has become known regarding the mechanism of such adaptations in general; pertinent information will be selected from the wealth of data available in the literature.[6]

It is clear that the adaptations discussed above fall under the general heading of variability. Now the flourishing science of microbial genetics has taught us many modes of microbial variation. The terms mutation, hybridization, recombination, and segregation at once suggest the many possibilities for arriving at changes in the genotype of the microbial cell. And because the very extensive and illuminating researches on *Neurospora* have laid such a solid foundation for the thesis "one gene, one enzyme," it is more or less self-evident that there has been a strong tendency to ascribe the appearance of a new enzyme in bacterial cells to a genetic change, that is, to a mutational phenomenon. I shall refrain from a detailed discussion of the consequences of this point of view, which will be dealt with in the next chapter.

Here it must be emphasized that a change in the enzymatic apparatus of a microbe may also be the result of a process in which each cell of a population is involved. In view of the fact that mutations have invariably been found to occur with an extremely low frequency, some biologists have felt an aversion against accepting an explanation of adaptive phenomena that is based on the hazards of a blind mutation. They find it more attractive to assume that a change in properties of a microbial population in response to a special environment is not the result of the spontaneous appearance of a genetically different cell which incidentally fits the new environment and then commands the situation, but rather that the environment induces each individual cell to change its physiological characteristics, for example, by causing it to develop a specific enzyme.

It seems worth while to review the main experimental data used by the defenders of the two contrasting theories; I choose as an example the adaptation of some fermenting bacterium to a new fermentation substrate.

The primary observations leading to the discovery of such a phenomenon—which is of quite common occurrence—can be summarized as follows. The investigator observes that, after a certain bacterium is inoculated into a suitable medium containing some sugar, good growth occurs and the sugar is readily fermented. In a corresponding medium containing some other sugar no fermentation whatever may occur. But now and then it happens that in a medium with yet a different sugar a negative result is at first obtained, though a vigorous fermentation may set in after a prolonged incubation; such a lag may even last for several days. Transfers from a culture in this stage to the same medium start to grow and ferment immediately. Obviously we must conclude that in this case during the incubation of the primary culture the properties of the bacterial clone have markedly changed.

I shall first consider some of the arguments that have been advanced by the supporters of the theory that the change involved is due to the interaction of the medium and the vast majority of the cells. A leader of this school is Hinshelwood,[7] who with his collaborators has studied several cases of adaptation such as that of a strain of *Aerobacter aerogenes* to *d*-arabinose. On inoculating about 10^8 cells in an arabinose-containing medium he observed a lag of 20 to 30 hours; in a corresponding glucose-containing medium growth could be established after about 2 hours. During the lag phase aliquots of the culture in the arabinose medium were simultaneously plated on two agar media, in which either glucose or arabinose were the sole source of carbon. The same number of colonies developed on corresponding glucose and arabinose plates; but on the former the colonies were observable after 17 hours, on the latter not till after 31 hours. This experiment at least clearly proves that *all* cells present in the lag-phase population are endowed with adaptive potentiality.

A further experiment tends to demonstrate that in the lag phase all cells are subject to a gradual transformation. On plating the population on a solid arabinose-containing medium at different times it was found, as is shown in Fig. 29, that the lag in the appearance of the colonies on these plates diminished progressively. It is indeed difficult to reconcile this outcome with the mutation

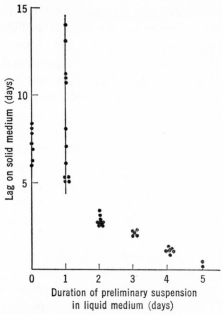

Fig. 29. Functional relation between time of suspension in liquid d-arabinose medium and lag shown by subcultures on solid medium. [From C. N. Hinshelwood, *Proc. Roy. Soc.* (*London*) B *139*, 62 (1951).]

theory, which implies the overgrowth of the initial population by a fully adapted mutant clone.

In another experiment the turbidity of a bacterial culture was followed during the lag phase, as shown in Fig. 30. It appeared that in the last part of the lag phase there was a sudden increase in density of not less than 40 percent, although microscopic counts showed that the number of the individual cells had not yet increased, multiplication occurring only some hours later. The observed increase in turbidity of the initial cell suspension, before a numerical increase of cells takes place, is difficult to reconcile with the mutant-overgrowth theory, but suggests strongly a more or less general participation of all cells of the inoculum in the adaptation process.

Finally, I wish to refer to yet another experiment in which a

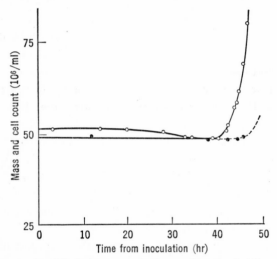

Fig. 30. Demonstration that increase in bacterial mass of culture precedes detectable multiplication of numbers. Carbon source: d-arabinose; open circles, mass expressed in terms of numbers of standard cells of the initial size; black circles, cell counts determined by direct counting and hemacytometer. [From C. N. Hinshelwood, *Proc. Roy. Soc.* (*London*) *B 139,* 65 (1951).]

quest was made for a hypothetical mutant. A suspension of fully unadapted bacteria was inoculated into an arabinose medium and at the same time streaked on a glucose medium. When the arabinose culture had reached the final stage of the lag phase, implying that multiplication had already set in and mutants should be numerous, the culture was again plated on glucose agar, and this operation was repeated 1 hour later. From each of the three glucose plates 27 colonies were isolated at random, and the lag time of each colony in an arabinose medium was established. It now appeared that the spread in lag time exhibited by the isolates from each of the three plates was practically identical. Apparently the adapted cells had all been "deadapted" on the glucose plate, a result that is difficult to explain on the mutation basis: the rate of a possible "back mutation" would have to have been incredibly high.

It is easily understood that such results have led Hinshelwood to the conclusion: "The experimental evidence now speaks decisively in favor of the view which attributes less importance to the hazards of cell division, and more to the direct interaction of the cells and the medium."

Nevertheless, Hinshelwood's views have met with considerable opposition. His opponents are prone to stress that Hinshelwood judges the adaptedness of the cells by establishing their ability to grow in a medium in which arabinose is presumed to be the sole source of carbon. Theoretically it would appear that under the circumstances the cell has to choose between two alternatives: adaptation to arabinose or death. In reality, however, the situation is markedly different, because in spite of the most rigorous precautions such media always contain small amounts of organic impurities. These will permit some growth of the test organism, and a population of 10^8, in which the probability of a mutation is far from negligible, may easily be reached. It is clear that this objection holds a fortiori when, for example, agar media are used. Consequently there is no doubt that several arguments advanced by Hinshelwood—although certainly not all—lose their force.

The advocates of the mutation theory of adaptation in sugar fermentation have, however, also made attempts to collect positive evidence in favor of their views. In this connection the very thorough study that Ryan [8] has devoted to the adaptation of *Bacterium coli mutabile* to lactose offers an excellent example.

This strain of *B. coli* deviates from the normal strains in its inability to ferment lactose during the normal test period. However, after a considerable lag time a vigorous lactose fermentation sets in. If now an isolation is made, a so-called lac+ culture is obtained which has a remarkable stability: even after 100 transfers on lactose-free media the ability to ferment lactose without significant lag is maintained.

These results raise the question what mechanism is responsible for the conversion of lac⁻ into lac⁺ bacteria? Like Hinshelwood, Ryan determined the frequency of this conversion by testing extreme dilutions of a suspension of lac⁻ cells for their ability to yield a lac⁺ culture. Fifty tubes with a medium containing lactose as sole carbon source were inoculated with equal quantities of a suspension which had been so highly diluted that on the basis of statistics 18 tubes could be expected to receive a single cell, and only 12 tubes more than one. It appeared that no fewer than 26 of the cultures entered into fermentation, thus proving that the adaptive power is widely distributed in the lac⁻ clone, and that a single lac⁻ cell frequently produces a lac⁺ clone.

This result is fully in agreement with Hinshelwood's analogous experiences. But Ryan's further experiments have convincingly demonstrated the occurrence of what he has called "background growth." He first showed that inoculation of agar plates—and even of thoroughly washed silica-gel plates—to which no organic substrate had been added leads to the development of microcolonies (Fig.31a), and next established that in sugar-free liquid media, prepared with extreme precautions against pollution, always a far from negligible growth also occurs. During the early stages the growth in such media is almost the same as in media with added lactose (Fig. 31b).

Nevertheless, Ryan found it possible by microscopic examination to differentiate between lac⁺ and lac⁻ bacteria on the basis of the size of the colonies produced on a solid lactose medium about 16 hours after inoculation. Figure 31a shows that at this time the background growth of a single lac⁻ cell has not produced more than 10^3 offspring; this practically eliminates the appearance of mutants prior to the moment of observation.

Next Ryan decided to study the influence of lactose on the chance of a conversion of lac⁻ into lac⁺ bacteria.

One way to determine the magnitude of this chance was given

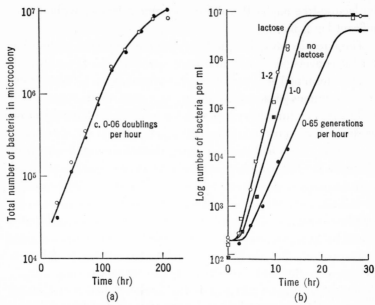

Fig. 31. (*a*) The growth of lac⁻ bacteria in a microcolony as determined by measuring the increase in diameter of 8 colonies on 1.6×10^{-4} M lactose agar (open circles) and 8 colonies on agar to which no carbon source has been added (solid circles). The colony diameters were converted into numbers of bacteria by use of the relation between diameter and bacterial number obtained by plating out microcolonies of different size from both types of agar. (*b*) The growth of lac⁻ bacteria in defined liquid medium with 1.6×10^{-3} M lactose (open squares and circles) and without lactose (solid squares and circles). The circles represent data obtained when routine procedures were used; the squares, when special precautions were taken to decrease the amount of contaminating carbon source in the defined medium. [From F. J. Ryan, *J. Gen. Microbiol.* **7**, 74 (1952).]

by the fact that on lactose agar lac⁻ microcolonies give rise to readily observable papillae whenever a lac⁺ bacterium is formed. If the number of bacteria in the colony is known, it is possible to calculate the mutation rate by counting the number of papillae on the colony. It is also possible to calculate, with the aid of the Poisson equation, the average number of papillae per colony from the number of colonies without papillae, as compared with the total number of colonies.

Using this method it could be established that the mutation rate was of the order of 10^{-7}, and was practically independent of the lactose concentration of the medium, and of the size of the colonies in which the change occurs.

The mutation rate of lac$^-$ bacteria in the absence of lactose was then determined with the aid of the statistical method developed by Lea and Colson. For this method it is necessary to start with a small number of bacteria. Ten milliliters of medium containing a growth-limiting amount of maltose were inoculated with approximately 1000 lac$^-$ bacteria, and 54 microcultures of 0.1 ml were made therefrom. After growth had ceased the total number of bacteria present in four of these microcultures was counted on a maltose medium. Each of the remaining cultures was integrally plated on a lactose medium and the resulting lac$^+$ colonies were then counted. The statistical evaluation of the result obtained yielded values for the mutation rate per generation that are indistinguishable from those observed in the presence of lactose. The reliability of the method employed was checked by various control tests which need not be discussed here.

It is easy to understand Ryan's conclusion that a spontaneous mutation is responsible for the adaptation of his strain of *Bacterium coli mutabile* to lactose. He criticizes also the arguments which Hinshelwood has advanced for the view that in his experiments on adaptation to arabinose changes in the vast majority of the cells are involved.

Quite recently a new publication of Hinshelwood [9] has appeared in which he reports on extensive experiments also dealing with the adaptation of a strain of *Bacterium coli mutabile* to lactose and in which he in turn subjects Ryan's study to a critical discussion.

I shall cite only one of his experiments. From a liquid lactose culture medium inoculated with the lac$^-$ strain plates were made on lactose agar at successive intervals during the lag phase. It was now found that the time for appearance of lac$^+$ colonies diminished with the length of the sojourn in the liquid medium, while at the same time the actual number of colonies on the plate did not change. It is clear that this again strongly suggests an interaction of the medium and the great majority of the cells.

I will not enter here into a full discussion of the controversy between Hinshelwood and Ryan. Hinshelwood rightly remarks that the controversial part of the field of bacterial adaptation has narrowed itself considerably of late years. The reason for this optimistic statement will become clear when we consider some other lines of development. They pertain to those investigations which have brought irrefutable proof that—under conditions which exclude a possible influence of genetical changes—the presence of certain compounds in a medium may induce the bacterial cell to the production of enzymes that were absent prior to this contact, at least in measurable quantities. It is this phenomenon for which Monod has introduced the name "induced enzyme synthesis."

At first sight the conclusion that such an induced enzyme synthesis exists seems to be justified as soon as one establishes changes in the metabolic behavior of a dense bacterial population in experiments of short duration. Under these conditions at least a mutational effect can be excluded. Taking into account that in all duly studied cases the mutation rate of bacteria has proved to be low—of the order of 10^{-7} or 10^{-8} per generation—it will be clear that the collective manifestation of a mass of, say 10^{10} cells, during an interval not exceeding a few generation times, cannot be measurably affected by mutant cells, owing to their small number (maximum about 10^3).

Stanier [10] was the first to study adaptation phenomena under such conditions more extensively. With the manometric technique he showed that a suspension of "resting" cells which causes a rapid oxidation of one substrate may initially be inactive to another, although after a brief incubation period the latter, too, is readily oxidized. The classical example given by Stanier is reproduced in Fig. 32; it shows that a clone of *Pseudomonas fluorescens* initially does not oxidize benzoate, but after about an hour starts to oxidize this substrate at an increasing rate. Evidently an en-

zyme system needed for benzoate oxidation is formed in consequence of the contact of the cell with this compound.

At least, this appeared to be the most plausible conclusion at
one time. However, I must not omit to remark that in analogous
cases its correctness has been challenged in later years. Various
observations have led to the discovery of a phenomenon that

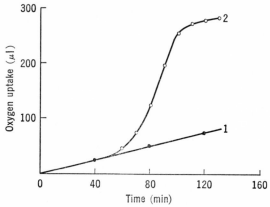

Fig. 32. Oxygen uptake with 2 micromols of benzoate by *Pseudomonas fluorescens* grown on yeast-extract agar; 1, autorespiration; 2, benzoate. [From
R. Y. Stanier, *J. Bacteriol. 54*, 341 (1947).]

might be aptly termed the "phenomenon of the masked enzymes."
It has been shown beyond doubt that certain substrates are attacked only after a considerable lag period by intact cells, while
these substrates are immediately broken down by disrupted cells,
that is, after the cells have been transformed into an enzyme
mash.

Figure 33, derived from a study by Repaske and Wilson,[11]
clearly shows this phenomenon for the oxidation of citrate by
Azotobacter agile. In view of the absence of any contrast in the
behavior of intact cells and that of enzyme preparations toward
other rather closely related oxidation substrates, neither the concept of a "barrier" which prevents the direct contact between
enzyme and substrate in the intact cell, nor that of a "carrier," en-

abling certain substrates to pass the barrier, seems to be very helpful in explaining this mysterious phenomenon.

Although these observations show that great caution must be exercised in interpreting adaptive behavior of "resting"-cell suspensions, there is not the slightest doubt that in many cases such phenomena are due to the formation of a new enzyme system. An example is the induced enzyme synthesis studied so penetratingly by Monod and collaborators.[12] These investigations are particu-

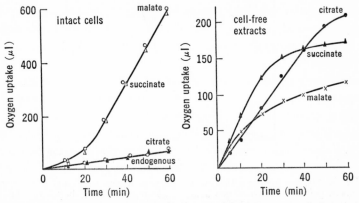

Fig. 33. The phenomenon of masked enzymes; the difference in behavior of intact cells and cell-free extracts of *Azotobacter agile* toward succinate, malate, and citrate. [From R. Repaske and P. W. Wilson, *Proc. Nat. Acad. Sci. U. S. 39*, 226 (1953).]

larly attractive because they deal with the formation of β-galactosidase in the cells of *Bacterium coli*, and are therefore directly connected with the behavior of related bacteria toward lactose discussed earlier. The French scientists have isolated the enzyme in a practically pure state, established its properties, and devised a quick and reliable method for its quantitative determination.

The starting point of Monod's investigation was the observation that a normal, that is, a lactose-fermenting, strain of *Bacterium coli* also starts growing and fermenting in a lactose medium only after a certain lag period. Monod now proved experimentally that bacteria grown in the absence of lactose lack β-galactosidase, but that, after incubation for some hours in a lactose-containing medium, such cells contain appreciable amounts of the enzyme. Lactose thus appears to act as a specific inducer for β-galactosidase synthesis, which proceeds only as long as lactose is present. In view of the short duration of the experiment and the very restricted increase in cell population, this result cannot be explained by the assumption that a spontaneous mutant endowed with β-galactosidase function had been selected for by the medium and outgrown the initial population. Moreover, in a recent publication Benzer [13] has demonstrated in a very ingenious way that, indeed, under suitable conditions the induced synthesis of β-galactosidase proceeds at a uniform rate in all the cells.

Monod further established that the inducer action is also possessed by other substances with galactoside configuration. To these belongs methyl β-*d*-galactoside, which is noteworthy since the strain used in this experiment attacks neither methanol nor galactose. At first all compounds that showed inducer action were found to be β-*d*-galactosides, but it soon appeared that the α-*d*-galactoside melibiose was also a fully satisfactory inducer. This observation was important because melibiose is not split by β-galactosidase. Obviously, the induction of enzyme synthesis does not require that the inducer itself, or one of its decomposition products, be a metabolizable substrate for the organism; this removes from the phenomenon of induced enzyme synthesis all teleological blots.

A further analysis of the induction phenomenon showed that, within a certain range, the rate of β-galactosidase formation is proportional to the concentration of the inducer. The minimum concentration for activity is very low: methyl β-*d*-galactoside acts in a concentration as low as 10^{-6} M (approximately 200 μg per liter).

It should be stressed that these several experiments show that for the formation of galactosidase one other condition should be fulfilled, namely, the presence in the medium of suitable carbon and nitrogen sources for protein synthesis. Accordingly, specific inhibitors of assimilation, like 2,4–dinitrophenol, inhibit the enzyme synthesis.

This point of view has since been found valid in all cases of induced enzyme synthesis. Bernheim and DeTurk [14] showed, for instance, that also in "resting-cell" experiments of the type initiated by Stanier the addition of ammonium ions and succinate markedly reduced the induction period, while various antibiotics in concentrations that did not affect the oxidation by the induced cells completely inhibited the enzyme synthesis.

The sum total of these observations leaves no doubt that in the case under discussion the formation of β-galactosidase, that is, of a specific protein, is strictly determined by an external factor, namely, the presence of an inducer in the medium.

At first sight this is a surprising conclusion, since in other cases it has been so convincingly proved that the presence of an enzyme is determined by the presence of one or more genes in the cell. The contrast is, however, more apparent than real. By ultraviolet radiation Lederberg obtained mutants that could no longer be induced to β-galactosidase formation by any of the inducers effective for the parent strain. Although the production of β-galactosidase by this strain is, therefore, a purely phenotypical affair, the significance of the gene for this process is very real. Apparently the presence of the gene does not automatically result in the formation of the enzyme, but it is requisite for its potential synthesis, which is accomplished if at the same time other conditions are fulfilled. It should be added that among the mutants obtained by Lederberg very strange deviations with regard to the factors determining β-galactosidase production were encountered. For instance, one strain was characterized by a spontaneous galactosidase production; for another strain β-methylgalactoside was a suitable inducer for the enzyme formation, although lactose was not metabolized—another example of the "masked-enzyme" phenomenon. As a result of numerous recombination experiments Lederberg concludes that at least seven different genes affecting the β-galactosidase production should be distinguished.

If now we consider the controversy in which Hinshelwood and Ryan are the main contenders in the light of the observations of Monod and his collaborators, it is difficult to escape the conclusion that in the adaptation of the bacteria to initially unattackable sugars induced enzyme synthesis plays an important role. But this does not exclude the possibility that the persistence of an adaptation after the removal of the inducer may be caused by a genetic change. This view is materially supported by the following elegant experiment of Cohen-Bazire and Jolit.[15] A strain of *Bacterium coli* for which induced β-galactosidase formation had been established was serially transferred (1) on lactose, and (2) alternately on glucose and lactose media. In the last series the clone was, therefore, continuously adapted and deadapted. After 10 to 15 transfers (approximately 500 generations) this clone appeared to consist of cells endowed with the ability of spontaneous galactosidase formation. Conversely, the majority of the cells grown continuously in the presence of lactose belonged to the type that formed β-galactosidase only in the presence of an inducer, at first sight a most paradoxical result. This result can, however, be explained if one assumes that the fate of mutants which can form galactosidase in the absence of an inducer differs in the two cases. There is no a priori reason to expect that such mutants would possess any selective advantage over the parent strain in the series of transfers on lactose media. This is not true in the other case; here the mutant, on transfer of the culture from glucose to lactose agar, can start growth at once, and thus outgrow the parent strain.

Cohen-Bazire and Jolit also arrive at a second noteworthy conclusion, that the number of mutant cells present in a normal noninduced population may well account for the trace of β-galactosidase that can be detected in this population. This would imply that the formation of β-galactosidase in an induction experiment takes place in cells which initially are completely devoid of the enzyme, in other words, that the induced enzyme synthesis is a formation *de novo*.

A second case of induced enzyme synthesis that has yielded information concerning the mechanism of inducer action has been described in a series of highly interesting publications by Pollock and collaborators.[16] These investigators studied the formation of the enzyme penicillinase in *Bacillus cereus*, for the synthesis of which penicillin is the only known inducer. A remarkable feature of this particular induction is that a very short contact between the cells and penicillin suffices; even after destruction of all accessible penicillin by adding penicillinase to the medium the cells continue to produce penicillinase. In exponentially growing cells the amount of penicillinase increases linearly after an initial lag (cf. Fig. 34).

Another characteristic point of the induction phenomenon is that penicillin production occurs even if the contact between the cells and the penicillin has taken place at 0°C and in the absence of an energy source, that is, under conditions that exclude enzyme synthesis. At the lowest penicillin concentrations that exert inducing effects (0.01 to 1 unit/ml) the rate of penicillinase production is proportional to the concentration of the inducer. These results strongly suggest that on contact of the cells with penicillin a small amount of the inducer is specifically fixed, and then persists in the form of a complex which controls the production of penicillinase.

Apparently we have here the remarkable situation of an agent producing an enzyme predestined to destroy one of its components; evidently the penicillin present in the complex is in some way protected against breakdown. Proof for the specific fixation of minute quantities of penicillin was furnished by experiments with penicillin labeled with radioactive S^{35}; the amount of S^{35} fixed was found to be proportional to the penicillinase-producing ability.

Finally we must mention that in a quite recent publication Pollock [17] stresses the occurrence of a small quantity of basal peni-

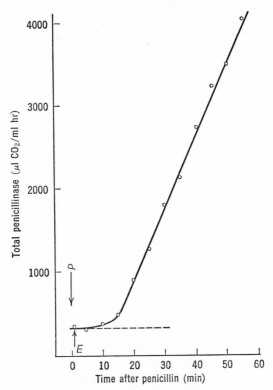

Fig. 34. Penicillinase production by a logarithmically growing culture of *Bacillus cereus* following addition of 1 unit/ml of penicillin (*P*) and subsequent destruction of all free penicillin by addition of active preparation of penicillinase (*E*). [From M. R. Pollock in E. F. Gale and R. Davies, ed., *Adaptation in Micro-Organisms* (Third Symposium of the Society for General Microbiology; Cambridge University Press, Cambridge, 1953), p. 161.]

cillinase in noninduced cells of his strain of *Bacillus cereus* and gives convincing arguments for the identity of this basal and the induced enzyme. This makes him reject the idea that induced synthesis of penicillinase should be a *de novo* formation.

On the basis of all the preceding and many additional observations, Pollock has advanced a general theory of the mechanism of induced enzyme synthesis. He stresses that the observations on penicillinase production make it difficult to avoid the conclusion that the penicillin reacts with some particular cell constituent, thus forming a complex, stable under ordinary conditions, which acts as a catalyst whose concentration determines the rate of penicillinase formation. Taking into account the facts known about β-galactosidase formation, Pollock has developed a concept, the essence of which he has summarized in a diagram which is represented in Fig. 35 in a slightly modified form. Though the nature

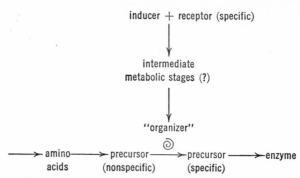

Fig. 35. Scheme of inducer action. [From M. R. Pollock in E. F. Gale and R. Davies, ed., *Adaptation in Micro-Organisms* (Third Symposium of the Society for General Microbiology; Cambridge University Press, Cambridge 1953), p. 156.]

and function of the organizer are not defined, its mode of action is envisaged as catalyzing the formation of a specific enzyme from a nonspecific precursor.

Evidently in the case of penicillinase the organizer is stable. In the case of β-galactosidase, in which a continuous supply of inducer is necessary to maintain a minimum concentration of the organizer, the latter is evidently quite unstable.

Pollock points out that in such cases the organizer must have a very rapid turnover, which could be more clearly understood if actually it functioned as a catalytic cycle with a heavy "wear and tear." The view that the instability of the organizer is primarily caused by its action is more or less supported by the observations of Koppel, Porter, *et al.*,[18] who discovered the phenomenon that they called "pretreatment induction." These investigators established that in a suitable induction medium, to which a small amount of chloromycetin was added, "organizer" was formed, but that galactosidase formation was inhibited. After the cells were transferred to a medium without chloromycetin and without inducer, enzyme formation set in, proving that the organizer had been stable as long as it was not functioning.

A more concrete explanation for induced enzyme synthesis was advanced by Yudkin as long ago as 1938. It involves the assumption that the enzyme is always present, though normally in amounts too small to permit its detection. The addition of a specific substrate would cause the formation of an enzyme-substrate complex, thus reducing the concentration of free enzyme, with the result that by mass action more enzyme would be produced. This explanation at once became doubtful after the discovery that inducers need not be substrates of the enzyme, and that enzyme substrates need not be inducers; an example of the latter type is furnished by Lederberg's studies on the behavior of some strains of *B. coli* toward neolactose; this sugar is split by β-galactosidase, but has no inducer action.

In any case, for the induced penicillinase formation Yudkin's theory has been rendered wholly untenable by the recent investigations of Pollock and Torriani [19] who successfully isolated penicillinase, and showed it to be a protein with a molecular weight of approximately 56,000. At 30°C the pure preparation decomposes 8.7×10^5 penicillin molecules per hour per milligram N, which means a turnover number (molecules of pencillin decomposed per molecule of penicillinase per minute) of 1.3×10^5. Moreover, the experiments with the sulfur-labeled penicillin have shown that 100 molecules of penicillin per cell are needed to induce penicillinase formation at maximal speed. These data permitted Pollock and Torriani to compute that within 60 minutes after induction each molecule of penicillin had caused the formation of at least 20 molecules of penicillinase. Obviously, this result precludes a stoichiometric combination of penicillin with some precursor molecule to form penicillinase, and the conclusion seems inevitable that a more or less transformed inducer in combination with some specific cell constituent acts as a catalyst in the enzyme-forming process.

The question then arises whether something can be said regarding the reaction chain leading to enzyme formation. The enzyme being a protein, there are two extreme possibilities: the enzyme is formed from a precursor protein without the coöperation of free amino acids or the enzyme molecules are built up completely from free amino acids. Finally, there is the intermediate possibility that the enzyme synthesis from a precursor is accomplished by a process requiring the incorporation of free amino acids.

This problem has recently been solved, mainly by the extensive studies of Halvorson and Spiegelman.[20] I shall mention here only one experiment on β-galactosidase formation in *Bacterium coli*.[21] By growing the organism in a medium containing labeled lactate as the sole carbon source, cells were prepared whose constituents were labeled throughout with radioactive C^{14}. The harvested crop was then introduced into a medium containing unlabeled lactate and an inducer of β-galactosidase formation. After a suitable period the cells were harvested and the β-galactosidase isolated from the extract obtained by disruption. A comparison was made of the radioactivity of the purified enzyme (calculated per milligram N) with that of the nonenzymatic protein obtained from the same source. It appeared that the enzyme exhibited less than 3 percent of the specific radioactivity of the nonenzymatic protein of the induced cells.

At the same time Hogness, Cohn and Monod [22] independently obtained almost identical results in experiments with cells previously labeled with radioactive sulfur.

These findings leave no doubt that in this case newly formed enzyme molecules are synthesized primarily from newly formed amino acids and that preëxistent precursors do not play a quantitatively significant role in the process of enzyme synthesis. It also implies that in the course of the induction no extensive break-down of cellular proteins to amino acids has occurred.

If I now try to summarize what the experimental data have to teach us I arrive at the following conclusions.

It has been proved with certainty that the metabolic properties of a bacterial clone, the progeny of one single bacterial cell, are liable to profound changes which enable the organism to thrive under extremely divergent conditions. In this respect *Micrococcus denitrificans* offers a most striking example of life's flexibility; it can grow equally well at the expense of some organic substrate in the presence of free oxygen as when it has to depend on the system molecular hydrogen–nitrate. But *M. denitrificans* by no means represents an isolated and rare case of adaptation; micro-biological literature abounds in reports which show that it is a general property of life to be able to change its enzymatic equip-ment, and in doing so to meet nature's challenges.

As for the causes underlying this flexibility, there can at pres-ent be no doubt that in many cases the observed changes are due to changes in genotype of the cell, and as such fall under the gen-eral notion of "mutation," the still so mysterious process which nowadays plays such an important role in all biological disci-plines and which can perhaps be studied nowhere better than in the microbe world. The discussion of this aspect of life's flexibility I leave to Dr. van Niel.

I have stressed that there are equally important changes in enzymatic equipment of the cell which proceed against a con-stant genetic background, to use the term coined by Spiegelman. There is no doubt that the phenotypical phenomenon of induced enzyme synthesis discussed in this chapter is of wide occurrence, and is to a high degree responsible for the surprisingly many-sided potencies of the living cell.

As for the way in which the inducer provokes the synthesis of a specific protein we still lack definite information. In the case of penicillinase the inducer apparently forms a stable complex which in principle continues its synthetic activity indefinitely. In the case of the β-galactosidase the complex evidently is unstable, since a constant supply from the medium is indispensable for a continuation of the enzyme synthesis. In the case of hydrogenase production by *Micrococcus denitrificans* the mere presence of molecular hydrogen as inducer does not suffice; the cell must be forced to a consumption of hydrogen by cutting off other routes of energy supply.

Although Pollock in his latest publication gives as his opinion that in induced enzyme synthesis we are as a rule not dealing with a *de novo* formation, yet it can be stressed that the phenomenon of induced enzyme synthesis has provided an opportunity to study the factors determining the synthesis of a protein whose specificity can easily be established owing to its enzymatic activity. Such a synthesis, which lies at the root of a characteristic property of the cell, is in some way governed by a gene, but apparently the potency of the gene remains dormant until it is aroused by the inducer. The way in which the coöperation of gene and inducer is carried into effect is certainly one of the most fascinating problems in biology, and Pollock has put forward highly stimulating considerations tending to show that a further penetration into this mechanism may lead to a better understanding of the problems of specificity, heredity and evolution.

The first successful in vitro synthesis of proteins from amino acids under the influence of bacterial preparations has just been announced by Gale and Folkes.[23] Especially the demonstration that the synthesis of a typical adaptive enzyme has been so accomplished, and that this requires the presence of both an inducer and nucleic acid—the latter being partially replaceable by its building stones—indicates that we may anticipate important developments in the near future.

Finally, I must point out that both Monod and Spiegelman [24] have rightly emphasized that as soon as the problem of differentiation in higher organisms is attacked at the cellular level there can scarcely be any doubt that the phenomenon of induced enzyme synthesis will be found to be of uppermost importance. The formation from one and the same fertilized egg cell of the various organs with their differences in metabolic activity seems to require the suppression of certain enzymes and the evocation of new ones against a genetic background which in principle is constant.

So I do not think I go too far in concluding that the studies on microbial adaptation, and more especially the discovery of the phenomenon of induced enzyme synthesis, represent another valuable present of the microbe to biology.

5

Trial and error in living organisms; microbial mutations

C. B. VAN NIEL

The Darwinian revolution in biological thinking resulted from the postulation of a mechanism that could account both for the enormous diversity of living organisms and for the undeniable relations between them that had been established by comparative anatomical and embryological studies. Such a mechanism was provided by the theory of evolution through natural selection. Obviously this theory presupposes the occurrence of differences among the component units of a population; the principle of the "survival of the fittest" is devoid of meaning unless all individuals are not equally fit.

That even the representatives of a single species do exhibit differences is, of course, a readily observable fact. At the time when the theory of natural selection was promulgated, next to nothing was known concerning the causes for variation among individuals. Consequently, this aspect was taken for granted, and the main problem confronting the evolutionist consisted in learning to understand better the mechanism of natural selection.

In the first chapter the microbe's contributions to a study of this problem have been emphasized. In particular, the application of elective cultures has shown that the ecologically significant qualities of the environment which permit a particular microbe to compete successfully with others can often be identified with special chemical or physical factors. It is true that in such experiments the investigator usually exposes a large variety of microbial types, introduced with the inoculum, to a defined environmental situation, so that the outcome provides the basis for assessing the selective advantages of the specific properties possessed by different types of microorganisms. Nevertheless, the same kind of selection by the environment should operate equally on the individuals of a single type, provided they, too, are different in one or more respects.

A perpetuation of properties offering selective advantages depends on their transmission from parent to offspring. When the nucleus had been recognized as the seat of heritable characteristics, and when mitosis had been discovered as the means by which their orderly transmission is achieved, it became clear that the problem had to be faced how differences in the properties of individual members of the progeny could arise. Studies pertaining to this aspect eventually showed that it can be accomplished under the influence of two essentially different sorts of mechanisms, designated as adaptation and mutation, respectively. In the preceding chapter the former has been stressed; it represents a change, induced by an external stimulus, that does not affect the nucleus. Consequently, adaptations are not generally considered heritable; it is merely the potentiality to adapt that can be inherited. From the point of view of evolution it is, therefore, more important that organisms are also known to undergo mutations, that is, changes in their nuclear composition, or in "genotype."

The mutation theory was launched by Hugo de Vries on the basis of experimental evidence later found by Lotsy to have been inadequate. It assumes the sudden appearance of genetically different individuals in initially homogeneous populations. In the course of half a century there has, however, accumulated so much cytological, genetic, and ecological evidence in its favor that it would be rash to challenge its reality.

It is still a matter of dispute what causes the nuclear changes. Muller's discovery that exposure of individuals to x-rays causes a considerable increase in mutation frequency, followed by Altenberg's studies on similar effects of ultraviolet irradiation and, more recently, by Auerbach's finding that sublethal doses of mustard gas produce the same result, have led to the idea that the naturally occurring mutations are likewise the result of some irradiation effects, or may be caused by environmental factors of a chemical nature. However this may be, the consensus of opinion seems to be that mutations are of relatively rare occurrence, and that fundamentally they are random events. It has furthermore been found that a large fraction of artificially induced mutants exhibit properties that can hardly be considered as beneficial in the struggle for survival; indeed, many such mutations are actually lethal. It seems reasonable to assume that this applies equally to the naturally occurring mutations.

The randomness of mutational changes exposes the aspect of *trial* in the behavior of living organisms. The element of *error* is made manifest by the frequent occurrence of mutants unable to compete successfully with the parent type. The latter feature has the implication of "waste," especially since so many of the products of mutation appear doomed to rapid extinction. Nevertheless, this insinuation may be little more than the expression of a characteristically human attitude in an age of efficiency. It might be well to contemplate the thesis that the development of something new, even in human endeavor, is generally the outcome of efforts many of which yield only negative results. To illustrate this point, let us consider the case in which the growth factor requirements of a microorganism are to be determined. The microbiologist has developed, as the most effective approach, a general methodology involving the simultaneous preparation of cultures in a large number of culture media, each one of which is deficient in a single vitamin, amino acid, purine, pyrimidine, etc. A simple inspection of the pattern of growth in the various media then permits a rapid decision as to the nature of the requirements. Now let us suppose that the result of such an experiment shows that biotin is the only essential growth factor. Obviously, in this event one single culture experiment in a medium containing biotin as the sole growth factor would have settled the problem. One might thus infer that the preparation of all the other cultures represents so much "wasted effort." But this is true only if the final answer is already known or suspected beforehand. An even more drastic situation is encountered if one wishes, for example, to isolate a new antibiotic agent. It is impossible to predict how many negative experiments will have to be undertaken in order to reach the desired goal. Yet I doubt whether anyone would be willing to brand these as "wasted." And if even the most rational approach that man has so far devised for reaching a better understanding of natural phenomena, namely, the scientific method, is based upon a gradual elimination of alternatives, it would, I believe, be better to refrain from using the term "waste," with its derogatory connotations, in connection with his efforts in this direction. For the same reason I am inclined to absolve the mutational phenomena from the stigma of "waste."

Regardless of the above considerations concerning their efficacy, however, we may regard mutations as a means of providing the raw material upon which natural selection can act. Studies in this field with higher organisms are time consuming and laborious, principally because of the large number of individuals required and the relatively extended generation times. It is, therefore, not surprising that *Drosophila* has for so long occupied a central position in mutation experiments; its generation time is short, and the handling of vast numbers of individuals is not too cumbersome. Nevertheless, studies on natural selection in mutant populations even of fruit flies have thus far not been vigorously pursued, owing to our lack of knowledge of ecological factors that may play a significant role as selecting agents.

These difficulties indicate that microbes, with a generation time measured in minutes or hours rather than in days, months, or years, with crop yields of 10^7 to 10^{10} individuals per milliliter of culture medium, and with much better understood nutritional requirements and general ecology, should prove to be even more favorable subjects for such studies—provided always that they, too, mutate.

Evidence in favor of this view has long been available. In an extensive paper, published more than forty years ago, Beijerinck described a number of curious observations under the title "Mutations in microorganisms." [1] The observations pertained to the appearance of secondary colonies, or "papillae," on top of primary colonies, and to the formation of sectored colonies with sharply distinguishable characteristics in the different parts, when pure cultures of several representative microorganisms were streaked on appropriate solid media. When special experiments showed that the cells from secondary colonies or sectors could be subcultured with maintenance of their respective properties, Beijerinck unhesitatingly ascribed their origin to mutations.

It must be admitted that the observed phenomena are fully consistent with this interpretation. The very concept of a mutation implies the sudden and random appearance, among the individuals of a normal population, of genetically aberrant cells capable of reproducing their own kind. These would thus become the foci for the development of a variant population, and the secondary colonies and sectors would represent the consequence of such continued growth under conditions of spatial fixation. Nevertheless, the possibility of accounting for the observations in this manner did not suffice to gain immediate and general acceptance for Beijerinck's ideas. For reasons to be mentioned below, many microbiologists were reluctant to think along these lines. But developments in microbiological research during the next twenty-five years gradually overcame the early skepticism, and once this stage had been reached, the obvious advantages of microorganisms for studies of mutational problems could be exploited.

The early investigations of microbial mutations dealt largely with a description of phenomena such as those mentioned above, and were thus concerned with the occurrence of morphologically distinguishable variants in pure cultures. In all such cases the culture conditions can be kept constant, a feature that eliminates the need for considering a specific influence on the organisms of some environmental factor as responsible for the observed effects. But gradually changes in physiological and biochemical properties commanded an even greater interest. This implied that growth in different media often became the best or even the only criterion for their recognition. In the preceding chapter it has been amply documented that an observed change in physiological characteristics need not be the result of a mutation, but may also be caused by the appearance of new enzyme systems whose formation is induced by special components of the culture medium. It is, therefore, imperative that the investigator of mutational phenomena which express themselves through physiological effects be in a position to distinguish sharply between the two alternative possibilities.

About twenty years ago I. M. Lewis analyzed this problem in connection with studies on lactose fermentation by *Bacterium coli mutabile*.[2] When grown in glucose media the bacteria could not ferment lactose; nevertheless, inoculation in lactose media yielded positive cultures in which the disaccharide was fermented. By simultaneously plating aliquots of glucose cultures on glucose and lactose agar, respectively, Lewis showed that about 1 in 10^6 individuals present in the glucose cultures was endowed with the ability to ferment lactose. Consequently the established facts were attributed to the occurrence of mutational events giving rise to the occasional appearance of a lactose-fermenting individual; in lactose media these individuals are selected for, thus accounting for the positive outcome of all cultures in lactose media. Nevertheless, no matter how reasonable this conclusion may appear, the discussion in Chapter 4 of the Hinshelwood-Ryan controversy must have indicated that there is still some room for doubt as to the validity of interpretations reached by means of such simple experiments.

It is therefore important to mention that in the course of time additional techniques have been devised for distinguishing between induced enzyme formation ("adaptation") and mutation as the underlying causes for observed variations in physiological behavior. One of these is the "fluctuation test" of Delbrück and Luria. It is based on the premise that a mutation, being a random event, does not follow a strictly regular pattern.

To illustrate the principle of this approach, let us consider the case of a culture of *B. coli mutabile*, growing in a lactose-free medium. It is possible, on the basis of Lewis's results, to predict that such a culture will contain lactose-fermenting mutant cells when the total number of bacteria in the culture has risen to 10^8. But it is very probable that in each of a large series of replicate cultures the number of such aberrant organisms is not the same, even though the total number of bacteria may be identical. Discrepancies in this respect could be expected if the first mutant appeared amidst the normal population at different times in the history of the individual cultures. Since the mutant cells can develop in the glucose medium side by side with the parent organisms, one should thus anticipate that at a later stage the mutants will have produced a number of offspring commensurate with the time of incubation after their initial genesis. Hence differential plating on glucose and lactose media of a large number of replicate cultures should reveal considerable differences in the total number of lactose-fermenting cells in the individual cultures if the acquisition of the ability to ferment lactose were the result of a mutation. Experiments by Delbrück and Luria have shown that the differences between such individual cultures is of the order of magnitude of one-hundred fold.

Two important variations of this methodology have been developed. The first one was invented by Newcombe in the course of studies on the origin of resistant cells in cultures of bacteria that normally undergo lysis when exposed to bacteriophage. The experiments were performed as follows. A number of culture plates were inoculated, each one with the same number of organisms, evenly spread over the surface. The plates were incubated for various relatively short periods of time, up to 6 hours, during which the inoculated cells developed into microcolonies. At these stages the presence of phage-resistant individuals was determined by spraying the plates with a phage suspension, followed by further incubation. It is clear that only the resistant organisms could subsequently grow out into macrocolonies, so that a simple count of the latter permitted an estimation of the number of resistant variants. These operations were, however, carried out in two different ways. Some of the plates were treated directly with phage particles, while others were first respread; this served to redistribute the individuals composing the microcolonies. The results showed that after the total number of bacteria on the plate had exceeded 10^8, the number of colonies on the respread plates was many times that on the plates exposed to phage without pretreatment, and that at an initial density of 3×10^9 cells per plate, the colony counts for individual respread plates differed by a factor of ten, while the counts on the companion plates were identical within the expected narrow limits of error. These results are fully compatible with the interpretation that the phage-resistant bacteria had originated, in a random manner, by mutation. In that event the mutated individuals would have appeared at different times, and thus produced microcolonies of different sizes on corresponding plates; the process of respreading served to increase the number of foci from which the macrocolonies could develop.

The second variant, known as the "replica-plating technique," we owe to the Lederbergs. It involves the preparation of a massive culture on the surface of a solid medium in the form of microcolonies from which transfers are made by means of sterile circles of velvet, mounted on wooden blocks. These are pressed down first on the film of growth and next on a different medium. The velvet serves as a consolidated mass of thousands of inoculating needles; the imprints on new media should thus represent transfers from vast numbers of microcolonies simultaneously. If the new media are inadequate for growth of the initial strain, the appearance of colonies on such media indicates that variants have sprung up; since it has been found that the distribution of macrocolonies on such media follows an identical pattern on duplicate plates, it must furthermore be concluded that on the "mother plate" microcolonies existed composed of organisms with the new properties. This phenomenon appears to be compatible only with the assumption that occasionally a variant with new properties appears among the members of a population, that is, with the occurrence of mutations. By using this technique for the inoculation of a number of different media, all unfit for the growth of the parent strain, Lederberg and collaborators have shown that in a pure culture with a population of 10^{10}–10^{11} individuals many different mutant types can be readily detected.

As a result of the application of these and other methods the evidence in favor of mutational changes in microörganisms—molds, yeasts, algae, bacteria, and protozoa—has lately increased to the point of leaving little doubt that they are of regular occurrence. This is most comforting because it implies that the trial-and-error principle is operative also in these organisms, and hence that the evolutionary notions of the "macrobiologist" can here be applied. It must, however, be realized that this conclusion has some unpleasant consequences as well. It is obviously disturbing to find that an unimpeachable single-cell culture, meticulously maintained in a pure culture collection, after several transfers appears to be composed of more than one type of organism. When, about ten years ago, our fairly extensive pure culture collection was lyophilized, well over 20 percent of the cultures, tested for purity prior to lyophilization, were found to contain at least two kinds of morphologically readily distinguishable variants. When a pure culture of a purple bacterium from our collection was recently investigated in Stanier's laboratory, it appeared to contain a number of types showing markedly different pigmentation patterns. And when an irreproachable yeast culture (*Schizosaccharomyces pombe*) from the Delft collection was analyzed by Leupold in Copenhagen, at least six different mutants could be isolated from it, and Leupold's own single-cell isolates contained more than one type after some months of subculturing. Such experiences are not rare; it is undeniable that we must learn to live with the fact that pure cultures cannot any longer be considered homogeneous in every respect after the population has reached a magnitude of about 10^8 cells, and this entails undesirable complications.

This is probably one of the reasons why it took so long before the idea of mutations in microorganisms was finally accepted. And, considering the developments in microbiological science, the reluctance of microbiologists to admit the existence of a high degree of variability, especially among bacteria, is fully understandable. Not only had it long been evident that the problems of an orderly classification of these organisms would be multiplied if one had to reckon with changes in the behavior of a pure culture, but it was also argued, on good grounds, that sloppy work can always be made to look more respectable by interpreting contamination as inherent variability. And when the bitter struggle of the adherents of the monomorphistic doctrine against the pleomorphists had apparently ended in a complete victory for the former, the outlook for a peaceful and rapid growth of the science was decidedly hopeful. Furthermore, and perhaps even more important, was the fact that a mutation, that is, a change of genotype, implies a change in the nuclear apparatus, and until the late 1930's it was highly doubtful whether microbes like the bacteria possessed a nucleus. One could, of course, maintain that the manifestation of heritable characteristics itself argued strongly in favor of the presence of a nucleus, but such reasoning by analogy does not constitute independent proof. Not until Badian and Piekarski learned to stain structures in bacteria that looked and behaved like nuclei, and Robinow finally perfected a methodology with which their demonstration became foolproof, was the existence of a true nucleus, though not necessarily of mitosis, finally accepted. Nevertheless, even this does not suffice to establish the reality of mutations.

With higher organisms, breeding experiments had provided a satisfactory means of substantiating the occurrence of nuclear changes, and hence of mutations. But it was generally held that most microbes cannot be crossed. This notion was changed when Winge and Laustsen rediscovered the existence of a diplophase in yeasts, demonstrated the feasibility of crossing these organisms, established Mendelian segregation in second-generation crosses, and incidentally found that physiological characters, such as the fermentability of various sugars, could serve as genetic markers. Soon afterward Beadle and Tatum embarked on their important studies with the mold *Neurospora*. From x-rayed conidia they isolated strains which differed from the original culture in that they required additional growth factors. By crossing experiments it was shown that the variant strains could be considered as single-gene mutants of the wild type. These investigations marked the beginning of the spectacular developments in the field of microbial genetics.

Subsequent experiments with bacteria showed that these organisms, too, respond to treatment with x-rays, ultraviolet light, or special chemicals, such as nitrogen mustard or hydrogen peroxide, by giving rise to clones with additional growth-factor requirements. The conclusion seemed obvious; even without supporting evidence from crossing experiments the strains with changed properties could be considered as single-gene mutants, comparable in every sense to those of *Neurospora*.

A few remarks may here be made concerning the methods for isolating such "nutritionally deficient" mutants. At first, this was a cumbersome procedure. In the case of *Neurospora*, for example, suspensions of conidia that had been treated with x-rays, etc., were plated out on agar media containing a complex mixture of growth factors, so that the mutants could grow out into colonies. Large numbers of colonies were then isolated, and each one was tested for changed nutrient requirements. Even with enormously increased frequency of mutational incidence, from 1 in 10^6 or more to 1 in 10^2, the number of mutants recovered was small, and rapid progress in the new field, dependent as it was on the availability of many mutant strains, could be made only in laboratories where considerable funds for technical assistance were available.

In consequence, a single individual might well hesitate before deciding to undertake such studies, unless more expedient techniques were invented.

Fries was the first to describe a method for the rapid separation of unchanged and nutritionally deficient mold strains. When inoculated into a medium that does not contain additional growth factors, only the former can grow; if the inoculation is performed with conidia, the wild-type conidia germinate and produce mycelial filaments. Because these are relatively large, they can be separated from nongerminated conidia by a simple filtration through filter paper. The viable elements in the filtrate, representing conidia that had not developed in the "minimal" medium, can then be grown on media with added growth factors, and each colony developing on such media is likely to represent a deficient mutant.

A comparable method was developed by Lederberg for isolating bacterial mutants with additional growth requirements. Because bacteria in the process of multiplication have approximately the same size as nongrowing cells, differential filtration obviously cannot be used to effect a separation of mutated and wild-type organisms. But by pouring plates of a minimal medium, inoculated with appropriate dilutions of cell suspensions treated with mutagenic agents, the unchanged individuals can be recognized as well-developed colonies after the plates have been incubated for some time, whereas the deficient mutants, unable to grow, have not produced colonies. After the position of the visible colonies is marked on the plates, a layer of agar with a supply af various growth factors is poured onto the original medium. Diffusion of the growth factors thus permits the mutant cells to grow out into colonies, and after further incubation these will appear, smaller than the colonies that had started earlier, and in new locations. Isolation of pure cultures from such colonies is thus apt to lead to "mutants only."

An elegant variant of this method has been introduced by Davis and, independently, by Lederberg. It is based on the use of antibiotics, such as penicillin, or of phage, which kill or lyse bacteria only during their multiplication. The execution of this method is as follows. A suspension of cells is inoculated into a minimal medium and incubated for a short time, after which the antibiotic or phage is added. The wild-type cells, which can grow in the medium, are killed off, whereas mutants, unable to develop, are unaffected. Subsequent plating of the cultures on complex media, if desired after elimination of the lethal agent by centrifugation and resuspension of the sediment, then yields colonies of those cells previously unable to grow, that is, of the "deficient" mutants.

Application of the last three methods can, of course, readily be combined with special procedures permitting the isolation by natural selection of mutants with predetermined nutritional deficiencies. For example, if a mass of nongerminated spores in the filtrate of a Fries-type experiment is inoculated into a minimal medium supplemented with a single vitamin, only those spores will grow for which this substance has become a new growth factor. Similar elective-culture experiments can be used in conjunction with the other methods.

Once bacterial mutants had become available, it was also possible to test the occurrence of sexual reproduction in bacteria. Such a phenomenon had occasionally been hinted at, but it had never been convincingly demonstrated. The first studies along these lines were carried out by Tatum and Lederberg with mutant clones, initially obtained from a single strain of *Escherichia coli,* and exhibiting different growth-factor requirements. According to present views, these clones could therefore be regarded as representing different single-gene mutants. A mixed culture of these two strains, when plated on "minimal" agar media, gave rise to colonies composed of wild-type cells. This result could be interpreted as indicating that exchange of genetic material between the two mutants, that is, a sexual process, had occurred. However, the incidence of such wild-type cells in the mixed culture was found to be very low, of an order of magnitude of 1 in 10^7 individuals. This rendered a sexual-fusion hypothesis precarious because the observed result could also be attributed to back mutations which often arise with a similar frequency. This consideration led to further experiments in which mutants with multiple deficiencies, obtained by treatment with mutagenic agents of the original mutants, were used in the same manner. Thus the frequency of back mutations to wild-type cells was reduced to levels so small that their detection by a regular plating procedure would be impossible. From mixed cultures of such multiple mutants wild-type cells were, nevertheless, recovered with a frequency of about 1 in 10^7. This result therefore supported the contention that hybridization was responsible for the assortment of genetic characters in new patterns.

Before this conclusion could be taken seriously, however, one other possibility had to be considered. The work of Avery and collaborators with different types of *Pneumococcus* cultures had shown that nucleic acids obtained from one type, when added to a culture of another type, could therein induce heritable transformations. Hence the appearance of wild-type cells in the experiments of Tatum and Lederberg with mixed cultures even of multiple mutants might have been the result of the excretion of similar "transforming principles" by one mutant and the subsequent induction of corresponding properties in the other. This possibility was investigated by Lederberg in an experiment in which three different, doubly deficient mutants with complementary characters were used (Table 12). The reasons for this choice of experimental material will become clear from the following considerations. If the genesis of wild type cells in the previous tests had been induced by diffusible transforming substances, it could be expected that cultures 1, 2, and 3, respectively, would excrete materials that could induce the appearance of A^+, B^+, and C^+ characters in the other strains. In that event wild-type cells should be found in a mixed culture of the three clones with a frequency similar to that observed in earlier experiments with but two multiple mutants. On the other hand, if a sexual process were responsible for the appearance of wild-type cells, the results would be quite different. This is so because any one sexual fusion might produce cells with the characteristics $A^+B^+C^-$, $A^-B^+C^+$, or $A^+B^-C^+$, but a completely wild-type organism could not arise except by subsequent fusion of two of these intermediate types. This implies that the maximum number of nondeficient organisms in mixed cultures of the three mutants should not exceed 1 in 10^{14}. Since Lederberg could not detect any wild-type cells in such mixed cultures, their formation as the result of an induction by diffusible substances appeared to be unlikely.

TABLE 12. SCHEMATIC REPRESENTATION OF LEDERBERG'S EXPERIMENT.

Culture number	Characteristics		
1	A^+	B^-	C^-
2	A^-	B^+	C^-
3	A^-	B^-	C^+

A similar conclusion was reached by Davis on the basis of experiments in which two different mutants were grown in two sides of a culture vessel, separated by a membrane through which bacteria could not pass. Under these conditions only an induction by means of diffusible transforming principles should be observable; and since no wild-type cells were found in these experiments, such a mechanism seemed precluded.

The case for segregation of genetic characters through nuclear fusion was further strengthened when Lederberg and collaborators discovered that mixed cultures of mutants occasionally give rise to colonies with peculiar properties. These colonies showed clear-cut patterns of segregation with respect to certain physiological characteristics, and this behavior could be perpetuated during many transfers. These observations suggested that the colonies in question might contain diploid cells which, during growth, would produce different types of haploid cells, each one becoming the starting point for the development of a sector with special characteristics. Microscopic examination of various parts of such colonies has provided support for this interpretation. Nuclear stains reveal the presence of structures strongly indicative of diploid cells, and stages that show a distinct resemblance to fusion products of two bacteria have also been observed.[3]

It should be mentioned that the success of the early studies on the existence of sexual processes in bacterial cultures was in no small measure due to a fortuitous selection of a particular *E. coli* strain. It soon appeared that the phenomenon of recombination and segregation of genetic characters in mixed cultures of two different mutants often failed to occur when other strains were used. But the initial impression that sexual reproduction in bacteria might be restricted to a very small number of strains has been effectively dispelled by later work. It has also become evident that bacteria can behave in a manner indicative of the occurrence of special "mating types," similar to those encountered in algae, fungi, and protozoa. Such bacterial mating types appear to be genetically controlled, as they are in the other groups of microorganisms.[4] Their existence may account for some of the negative results of "crossing" experiments.

After the recombination of genetic characters had been discovered in bacterial cultures, studies were soon initiated to determine whether bacteriophages behave in a similar manner. It had already been found that mutagenic agents can induce heritable changes in these viruses, and experiments with "mutant" phages, especially by Luria and Dulbecco, have established the occurrence of recombination also for these entities.

From the foregoing discussion it may have been surmised that the transmission of heritable characteristics from parent to offspring, and the appearance of new genetic properties through mutational changes, both proceed in an essentially identical manner in the microbes and in the higher plants and animals. This may well be the case. However, in that event the "macrobiologist" should be alerted to watch the behavior of his experimental material in order to determine whether it exhibits features that have so far been studied in some detail only with microorganisms.

It was in experiments on recombination of genetic characters with two mutant strains of bacteria that Hayes [5] discovered a phenomenon which is difficult to reconcile with the occurrence of a conventional sexual process. He found that it is possible to recover cells with wild-type characteristics from mixtures of two multiple mutants even if the cells of one of the two clones are killed by streptomycin or ultraviolet irradiation. He subsequently established that it is by no means immaterial for the outcome of the experiments which of the two partners is so killed. Recombination occurred only if one particular strain was subjected to the lethal treatment; if the other mutant was destroyed, no exchange of properties was observed. With the proper clone killed, the extent of recombination could even be several hundred times what it was when this strain was used in the living state. When next it was shown that the mutant in question carried a latent phage, absent in the other strain, the concept developed that the phage, which is liberated when the cells die, may carry genetic material from the former, the "donor" strain, to the latter, the "acceptor."

Essentially the same discovery was made independently by Lederberg and collaborators in studies with *Salmonella* mutants. The pertinent experiments revealed that genetic traits can be transferred from one mutant strain to another under conditions precluding direct contact between the cells of the two clones by growing them in the two sides of a U-shaped tube, separated by a bacterial filter. Here, too, the transfer was found to be unilateral, and associated with the presence of a phage in the donor strain.

At first sight these phenomena might suggest the operation in bacterial cultures of a fertilization mechanism by sperm cells, quite analogous to that encountered in higher plants and animals, and with the phage acting in the capacity of sperm. Nevertheless, the analogy is far from complete. For such a mechanism leads to the merging of the entire genetic complement of one individual with that of the other, meiosis being responsible for the subsequent sorting out of the parental genes. In bacteria it has, however, been found that frequently only a single heritable property, or gene, of the donor strain is introduced into the acceptor clone. This characteristic, for which the term "transduction" has been coined, is reminiscent of the earlier-mentioned transformations in *Pneumococcus* cultures, discovered about fifteen years ago by Avery and collaborators, and of the transmission of hereditary properties by means of particles that have no obvious direct connection with the nuclear apparatus, as found in the extensive studies of Sonneborn with protozoa, and of Ephrussi *et al.* with yeasts.[6]

It must be admitted that the occurrence of such phenomena in various microorganisms does not suffice to justify the conclusion that they should also be encountered in the higher plants and animals. Nevertheless, an awareness of these discoveries should induce the "macrobiologist" to examine their potential implications for the formulation of new hypotheses that might account for certain aspects of the behavior of his experimental material.

Thus far the most notable contributions that have come out of studies with microbial mutants have been in the field of biochemistry. This was initiated when Beadle and Tatum interpreted the requirement for new growth factors of mutant strains of *Neurospora* as the result of blocks in the chain of reactions that lead to the synthesis of an indispensable cellular constituent, P_n, from ingredients of the medium. It may be supposed that the original strain can accomplish this synthesis by means of a series of reactions, each one controlled by a special enzyme, a process that can be schematically represented as follows:

$$\text{substrate} \xrightarrow[\text{enz.}_1]{} P_1 \xrightarrow[\text{enz.}_2]{} P_2 \xrightarrow[\text{enz.}_3]{} P_3 \xrightarrow[\text{enz.}_4]{} P_4 \xrightarrow[\text{enz.}_5]{} P_5 \cdots \xrightarrow[\text{enz.}_n]{} P_n.$$

According to this line of reasoning, a biochemically deficient mutant should then be able to grow just as well if supplied with P_n as with any one of the intermediate products occupying a position in the reaction chain following the "block." This has been experimentally verified; mutants with a common requirement for P_n could be distinguished by their ability to use, instead of the end product, different postulated precursors. This, together with the fact that a mutant unable to grow, for example, at the expense of P_2, but normally developing in media containing P_3, P_4, . . . , often produced from the substrate considerable amounts of P_2, lent valuable support to the above interpretation of an enzymatic block in a biosynthetic reaction chain. And when crossing experiments indicated that each mutant differed from the parent strain by a single gene, it was logical to conclude that each gene controls the synthesis of one particular enzyme. The fruitfulness of this concept cannot be in doubt. By permitting the determination of the chemical nature of numerous intermediate products, studies with nutritionally deficient mutants have greatly extended our knowledge of the detailed mechanism of many biosynthetic reactions, and further progress in this field may be confidently expected.[7]

But some experiments of this kind have also shown that not all mutations are readily interpretable with the aid of the one-gene-one-enzyme hypothesis. I shall leave aside the "morphological mutants," whose characteristics have not yet been subjected to a detailed analysis, and confine myself to a consideration of two examples of apparently typical biochemically deficient mutants. The first is provided by the studies of Strauss with a *Neurospora* mutant unable to develop in a medium that satisfies the requirements of the parent strain, but exhibiting normal growth if the ammonium salt, adequate as the sole nitrogen source for the wild type, was replaced by any one of a number of amino acids. This result, quite unexpected on the basis of the one-gene-one-enzyme hypothesis in conjuction with current concepts of the mechanism of amino acid synthesis, led to a further investigation which showed that the mutant actually can use ammonia nitrogen provided the culture medium is sufficiently alkaline.

The other instance is furnished by the work of Doudoroff and McGee with *Pseudomonas saccharophila*. This bacterium cannot oxidize glucose or fructose; but mutants have been isolated that can do so. Examination of enzyme extracts from wild-type and mutant strains has shown that these may contain all the enzymes needed for the oxidation of the sugar. Hence the behavior of the parent culture cannot be attributed to the absence of an enzyme immediately concerned in the oxidative degradation. In the preceding chapter Professor Kluyver has emphasized the fact that comparable situations have been encountered in cases where "adaptations" rather than "mutations" are involved.

It is, of course, possible to account for such results by postulating that the inability to metabolize a compound may be connected with factors that prevent the establishment of direct contact between substrate and enzyme. Thus, permeability barriers and special organizational patterns of enzyme systems have been invoked to explain the difference in behavior of intact cells and enzyme extracts. It can further be argued that even in these cases the one-gene-one-enzyme concept need not be abandoned, because specific enzymes may well be responsible for the maintenance or generation of the requisite structural features. Without denying the usefulness of such interpretations as a guide to further investigation, I believe, however, that it is important to realize that at present they represent little more than verbal paraphrases of observed phenomena, and do not add appreciably to our comprehension of the mechanisms involved.

The great majority of microbial mutants used in biochemical studies have been typical "loss mutants"; they lack some property possessed by the wild type. This, along with similar experience obtained from studies with higher plants and animals, has occasionally led to the notion that all mutations perforce imply losses. In those few cases where an obvious "gain" is encountered, as for example, in Lewis's lactose-positive *E. coli mutabile* mutants, it is possible to account for the appearance of the new property by assuming that the non-lactose-fermenting parent culture was itself a loss mutant of a naturally occurring clone, especially because all typical *E. coli* strains do ferment lactose. The lactose-positive mutant would thus represent a mere reversion to the normal type, an atavist. Mutants of other microbial species which, in contrast to their wild-type parents, are resistant to phage, antibiotics, etc., can be similarly interpreted.

It is, however, difficult if not impossible to account for evolutionary events on such a basis, which would imply that the first organism should have possessed all the characteristics now encountered among the vast number of representatives of the plant, animal, and microbial worlds. That only loss mutants should arise, even as a result of treatment with mutagenic agents, seems, therefore, unlikely. And the general impression that this is, nevertheless, the case may well be connected with the special methodology employed for the isolation of biochemically modified types. As long as these are selected by such procedures as those used by Beadle and Tatum, Fries, Davis, and others, one can hardly expect to become confronted with "gain mutants." Although theoretically it is possible to conduct experiments with the specific purpose of detecting the presence of "gain" mutants, the execution would be anything but simple. Some of these matters will be discussed in more detail in the last chapter.

Conversely, the successes scored in biochemical investigations with microbial mutants have greatly aided in overcoming the early aversion to the notion that microbes, too, mutate, a notion that is now generally accepted. In addition, they have provided strong support for the ingenious hypothesis with which, as early as 1912, Twort and Ingraham approached the problem of growth-factor requirements by microorganisms. It was based on the assumption that a parasitic bacterium, unable to grow in media commonly used for the cultivation of closely similar but non-parasitic forms, might have lost the ability to synthesize some vitally important cell constituent through constant association with a host which normally supplies this substance. Lwoff in particular has developed this concept further, and indicated how it can serve to trace evolutionary trends among microbes with comparable morphology and ontogeny, but different nutritional patterns.[8] Without defending the thesis that all microorganisms with complex growth-factor requirements should be considered as nutritionally deficient mutants of less exacting types, it must be conceded that the former often do arise through mutation. And their mere existence in nature implies that they can successfully compete with the wild-type counterparts, in spite of their dependence on a more complex environment. It need hardly be mentioned that this consequence should ultimately be interpretable on the basis of the principle of natural selection, and it is easy to see that a slightly increased rate of growth, or a greater resistance to metabolic products or other inhibitory agents, for example, could be invoked to account for the persistence of deficient mutants. Even though relatively little attention has thus far been paid to this problem, the experiments of Atwood *et al.*, of Novick and Szilard, and of Braun have already provided striking examples of natural selection of mutants by just such mechanisms.

Apart from genotypic variants clearly recognizable as "nutritionally deficient," many others occur which, for the time being, can best be designated as "morphological" mutants. This category includes those variants which, on solid media, produce colonies distinguishable from the colonies of the original type. That such mutants can also establish themselves in competition with the wild type is shown by the fact that pure cultures, after a number of transfers, so often give rise to more than one kind of colony.

A special case in point is presented by the frequently encountered "rough-smooth" variation in bacterial cultures, once attributed to "dissociation" and "life cycles." For many years these terms have plagued microbiologists who could find little comfort in the vague connotations conjured up by their use. The masterly analysis of Braun [9] has done much to bring the observational evidence in line with an interpretation on the basis of the concept of mutation and natural selection.

Eventually it may become possible to associate both the morphological characteristics of such mutants, and the selective mechanisms whereby they established themselves, with specific physico-chemical factors. When this has been achieved, it will perhaps be evident that the results are also of significance for a more profound understanding of certain aspects of morphogenesis in higher organisms. Professor Kluyver has already stressed the importance of environmentally induced enzyme synthesis in connection with this phenomenon (see Chapter 4). In view of the large number of cells of which the higher plants and animals are composed, it would, however, not be surprising to find that mutational changes, too, may be involved.

From the above discussion it will be obvious that the "trial-and-error" principle plays an important role in the behavior of microbial cultures. Changes in genotype can be produced through mutation, hybridization, and transduction, thus yielding the varied raw material for natural selection to act upon. This situation also has important implications for the problem of classification of microorganisms.

Many serious attempts have been made to arrive at an orderly arrangement of the vast number of microbial types that can be distinguished by the particular characteristics they exhibit. Such an arrangement, together with a stable system of nomenclature, should provide the microbiologist with the means whereby he can identify his isolates and designate each culture possessing a special combination of properties by an appropriate, simple name.

Now, it does not require much perspicacity to realize that an effective system of classification must be based on criteria that are not variable. Unfortunately, it seems that in the past very little attention has been paid to this requirement, especially in connection with the classification of bacteria. New "species," and even "genera," have been proposed for clones that do not differ from similar ones by more than a single characteristic, and it is often difficult to dismiss the apprehension that the distinguishing features could easily be the expression of mere single-gene differences.

This is not the place to review the many problems that confront the bacterial systematist. There is, however, one particular aspect that may be briefly discussed in connection with our present knowledge of microbial mutations. It pertains to the existence of certain groups of bacteria whose members display so varied a distribution of characteristics as well-nigh to defy any reasonable approach to their classification.

When a bacteriologist isolates a large number of strains of, for example, fluorescent pseudomonads or aerobic spore-forming bacteria, by conventional methods from natural sources, he often finds that practically every clone can be distinguished from all others by one or more properties. In order to indicate the multitude of patterns in which the differential characters occur, he may resort to the expedient of proposing a different specific name for each of his strains. Such a practice is, however, unsatisfactory because, as a rule, it does not permit the identification of additional isolates except by considering them, too, as new species. It has therefore been criticized by the "lumpers," who believe that it is procedurally sounder to use a specific epithet only as a means of designating a combination of several, preferably independent, characteristics. Although there is much to recommend this attitude, its application is not free from the stigma of arbitrariness. The latter could be minimized if it were possible to understand the reasons for the existence of so many intermediate types.

In this connection attention should be drawn to some recent advances in the interpretation of species formation in higher plants and animals. The "macrobiologist" has recognized the important role played by prolonged hybridization among individuals growing in neighboring areas, and subsequent spatial separation. During the period of unrestricted interbreeding he has found in the conjoint environments a great variety of types which represent a virtually continuous series of intermediate forms between a number of extremes which can readily be distinguished because they differ in several respects.

Is it too audacious to suggest that the microbiologist may be facing a similar situation when he encounters among his broadly defined groups equally baffling combinations of characteristics?

Now that transmission of heritable properties between different bacterial clones in mixed cultures has been firmly established, it seems to me that this possibility is far from remote. If a detailed analysis were to provide support for this contention, a better approach to the taxonomic problems that these groups present might be found. Besides, a study of the selective influence of special environmental factors on the members of such groups could aid in interpreting their behavior in the laboratory and in nature, and thus in evaluating the forces involved in species formation, even in the higher forms of life.

It will be apparent that much remains to be done in the field of microbial genetics. But it should be remembered that nearly all the significant advances have been made during the last decade, and they are already impressive.

By showing themselves to be subject to mutational changes, the microbes have enabled the biologist to probe into the operation of the "trial-and-error" principle with experimental material which, on account of its short generation time and the ease with which vast numbers of individuals can be handled under controlled conditions, stands out as exceptionally favorable. These probings have revealed that hereditary traits can be transmitted by means other than nuclear fusion and meiosis. They have indicated that greater dependence on a complex environment may be accompanied by an increased rate of growth, or by a higher degree of resistance to unfavorable conditions, thus providing valuable information concerning the mechanisms whereby natural selection allows "deficient" mutants to maintain themselves in competition with less exacting types. They have led to the concept of a close interrelation between genes and enzymes, and to its further exploitation for the acquisition of a more profound understanding of the mechanism of biosynthetic reactions.

Finally, these accomplishments have exerted a fertilizing influence on the speculations concerning the fundamental problem of evolution and the origin of living organisms. This aspect will be treated in the concluding chapter.

6

Evolution as viewed by the microbiologist

C. B. VAN NIEL

In the preceding chapters we have attempted to sketch some developments of microbiological research which, in our opinion, have significantly expanded our knowledge of the basic characteristics of living organisms, and to indicate how this, in turn, has permitted the formulation of a number of concepts that have exerted a decisive influence on general biology by serving as guides in devising fruitful approaches to various problems. These developments may be summarized as follows:

1. We have become familiar with the existence of an enormous variety of microorganisms, exhibiting a range of physiological and biochemical properties far beyond that normally considered by the "macrobiologist."

2. Underlying this vast diversity of properties a unifying principle can be recognized, and this has made it possible to develop increasingly comprehensive concepts regarding physiological and biochemical processes, so that the specifically different ones can all be interpreted in terms of "variations on a theme."

3. It has been found that the same general concepts are also applicable to the members of the plant and animal kingdoms.

4. The pattern of behavior of microorganisms is not fixed but flexible; it can be modified by environmental factors which may induce the appearance of a new characteristic in a genetically constant cell.

5. A variation in properties may also result from sudden and random changes in genotype, with subsequent selection by the

environment of those modified entities which can successfully compete with the original type, thus illustrating the operation of the "trial-and-error" principle in the world of microbes.

These points support, in an almost compulsory manner, the concept of the relatedness of all forms of life and the monophyletic origin of the multitude of living organisms known to us today. The occurrence of different types can best be attributed to the processes of evolution and natural selection. The comparative simplicity of the microbes further suggests that these creatures must occupy a position somewhere near the base of the evolutionary scale, a conclusion which imposes upon the microbiologist the duty to attempt a solution of the problem of the manner in which the microorganisms themselves might have come into existence. This problem has been the subject of many speculations and investigations. Especially the important contributions made during the second half of the nineteenth century have been instrumental in causing most scientists to deny the occurrence of a "spontaneous generation" of these creatures. Nevertheless, this has led to a philosophically unsatisfactory situation which it will be my task to evaluate.

Assuming at least a rudimentary knowledge of the somewhat diverting history of the notions concerning the origin of living organisms, I shall not review the experiments which, by gradual stages, forced the "natural philosophers" to search for bona fide evidence in favor of a spontaneous generation of ever smaller organisms. Suffice it to start with the outcome of the imaginative studies of Pasteur, the chemist, and Tyndall, the physicist, which had provided the basis for the contention that even bacteria, the smallest organisms known at that time, do not appear in media previously recommended for the demonstration of a spontaneous generation, if the ever-present contaminants are first destroyed, and subsequent ingress of living germs is prevented by appropriate measures. During the 1930's the same conclusion was reached regarding the still smaller autonomic entities, the viruses. Thus the scientist was confronted with a problem that

Samuel Butler had appreciated more than fifty years ago when he made the significant entry in his notebooks:

> You may assume life of some kind omnipresent for ever throughout matter. This is one way. Another way is to assume an act of spontaneous generation, *i. e.*, a transition somewhere and somewhen from absolutely non-living to absolutely living. You cannot have it both ways. But it seems to me that you must have it both ways. You must not begin with life (or potential life) everywhere alone, nor must you begin with a single spontaneous generation alone, but you must carry your spontaneous generation (or denial of the continuity of life) down, *ad infinitum*, just as you must carry your continuity of life (or denial of spontaneous generation) down *ad infinitum* and, compatible or incompatible, you must write a scientific Athanasian Creed to comprehend these two incomprehensibles.[1]

In the course of time some attempts were made to account for the presence of living organisms on earth by proposing that life had been introduced from other parts of the cosmos, by being carried in or on meteorites, or propelled through outer space by light pressure, for example. It will, however, be obvious that these notions are hardly more than subterfuges; as Tyndall rightly remarked: "Such ideas merely serve to banish the investigation of the question to some conveniently inaccessible corner of the Universe." It is, therefore, imperative to reëxamine the situation if we wish to find a more satisfactory solution of the problem. The microbiologist in particular must be aware of this need on account of his preoccupation with biological material apparently reasonably close to the "beginnings of life," and at the same time because he is more immediately responsible for the impasse resulting from his failure to demonstrate spontaneous generation. And at present he is apt to accept the opportunity to discourse on this matter with the more alacrity since the significant ideas on the subject, developed during the last few decades, have placed him in the favorable position of being able to defend the thesis that life started as a result of spontaneous generation without having to abandon his belief that it has not been demonstrated, and that its actual occurrence may not be verified for a long time to come.

For, in spite of the evidence against "biopoesis," the useful term recently coined by Pirie to designate "the creation of something, that some people might wish to call living, from nonliving material," microbiologists, like most natural philosophers, have always been loath to reject the idea that at one time it may have occurred. According to Dubos,[2] even Pasteur himself realized that his incisive experiments could not be used to argue against this possibility. This stand is, of course, scientifically sound, based as it is on the recognition that a negative result can never justify the conclusion that a looked-for phenomenon does not exist; lack of knowledge of special conditions under which it might occur can always be invoked to explain negative findings.

Now, the newer concepts are important partly because they make the earlier failures comprehensible, partly also because they are in line with present-day knowledge of biochemical events. In this respect they contrast favorably with previous attempts which, based on an acceptance of biopoesis, were concerned with speculations on the probable nature of the first living organisms on earth. The starting point for these speculations used to be the idea that the earth was a purely mineral environment at the time when it had sufficiently cooled to sustain life. Such an environment is, of course, unsuitable for the growth of any but the chemo- and photoautotrophic organisms. This led to the conclusion that microbial representatives of these groups had to be considered as the most likely progenitors of all other forms of life. Only after the former had produced organic matter from the inorganic constituents of the earth's atmosphere and lithosphere was an environment created in which organisms with requirements for organic substances could grow.

Ostensibly this sort of reasoning satisfies the demands of the evolutionary theory in which the more complex is derived from the simpler. Nevertheless, there is a serious flaw in the argument, and this has become more and more obvious as our understanding of biochemical reaction mechanisms has increased. We have learned to interpret these mechanisms as chains of step reactions, each one controlled by a specific catalyst or enzyme, and we have come to think of differences in nutritional requirements in terms of differences in synthetic ability of the organisms concerned. The evidence provided by studies with a wide variety of microbes even suggests that the greater is the biosynthetic capacity of an organism, the more elaborate must be its enzymatic composition. From this it follows that the chemo- and photo-autotrophs, which exhibit the greatest biosynthetic ability known to us at present, must possess a vast array of enzymes. Once this is granted, it is also clear that such an organism cannot be considered as "primitive," and that we must qualify as wholly inadequate the concept that the first living creatures were of this kind. The evolutionary approach to biopoesis dictated the need for starting with a simple system. But the above analysis shows that the selection of the *environment* for this purpose entails the inevitable consequence that the first *organism* must have been exceedingly complex.

This difficulty can be avoided if we start at the other end, and postulate the genesis of a simple organism in a complex environment. Such an approach was first proposed by Haldane, in 1928,[3] although Darwin had apparently considered this possibility in a tentative manner half a century earlier, as pointed out by Hardin.[4] In a much more elaborate form it was later advocated by Oparin, whose book on the origin of life [5] has greatly accelerated the dissemination of this general idea.

Haldane's hypothesis, that the first living entity was an organism with little or no biosynthetic activity, is much easier for present-day biologists to accept than the earlier "autotroph hypothesis." Its corollary is, however, that the fundamental difficulty inherent in the latter has merely been displaced, because the "heterotroph hypothesis" requires the existence of a very complex environment. This implies that the evolutionist must devise a mechanism whereby a simple environment could have been changed to a complex one. At present there is a general tendency to attribute such a change to various kinds of chemical reactions, a process which may be termed "chemical evolution." The notion of a chemical evolution preceding a biological one is in itself not without appeal; in fact, it can be even further extended by interpreting the successive events taking place in isolated parts of the universe as the result of a sequence of physical, chemical, and biological evolutions. If we consider the fact that at the highest temperatures matter exists largely in the form of elementary particles, such as electrons, protons, neutrons, and mesons; that at lower temperatures atoms are found; and that in yet cooler environments molecules occur, such a sequence readily suggests itself. By extrapolation this approach then leads to the concept that simple molecular species can yield more complex ones under the influence of various sorts of radiation, of temperature fluctuations, etc., by different kinds of chemical interactions. It is certainly not inconceivable that in this manner numerous types of organic compounds could have been formed from inorganic substances, and the recent work of Miller and Calvin has adduced experimental evidence for the existence of just such conversions. They have shown that a mixture of H_2O, NH_3, CH_4, and H_2, exposed to electric discharges, contained identifiable amino acids, such as glycine and alanine, within a few weeks,[6] and that 6- and 8-carbon compounds can be formed from H_2O, NH_3, CO_2, and other simple molecules supposed to have been among the earliest constituents of the earth by high-energy radiation from a cyclotron.[7] In view of the fact that recent estimates of the age of the solar system agree on a limit of about 5,000 million years, it is clear that time was not wanting. Thus a prolonged chemical evolution could eventually have resulted in the formation of increasingly complex molecules. There is no reason to assume that the reactions involved would have been other than essentially random; in this respect they would be comparable to the "trial-and-error" events now generally accepted as the basis of biological evolution.

The objection may be raised that organic matter is not stable enough to permit a chemical evolution to run its course until a sufficiently complex mixture of organic substances had been formed so that biopoesis could occur. It has, however, been pointed out by Haldane, Oparin, and subsequent writers on the subject that this objection is not strictly applicable to the situation. To be sure, organic substances are often found to decompose rapidly. But it must be remembered that this is usually the result of chemical reactions in which molecular oxygen takes a part, or of biological processes. Hence the stability of organic matter in the absence of oxygen and of living organisms is of a very different order of magnitude. There is good evidence in favor of the view that the oxygen in the earth's atmosphere did not appear until photosynthesis had evolved. Thus, prior to the advent of biopoesis, organic compounds should have exhibited the same degree of stability as they do, for example, in canned products.

The concept of biopoesis in a complex environment presents yet another difficulty. The ultimate formation by chemical evolution of a sufficiently varied assortment of organic substances for spontaneous generation to occur can be expected only if the products of the initial reactions can be brought into close contact with one another. Since they are apt to be formed in extremely high dilutions, a preliminary concentration will be required. A simple means whereby this can be achieved is adsorption on finely dispersed inorganic matter, such as clay, and this has been suggested by Bernal[8] and Goldschmidt[9] as an adequate auxiliary hypothesis. Goldschmidt has even proposed that orientation on crystal faces of anisotropic substances might account for the separation of optical antipodes.

It thus appears that the general idea of a progressive physical, chemical, and biological evolution is not incompatible with current knowledge. It is beyond the scope of this chapter to discuss what sort of reactions might have occurred during the various stages of the postulated chemical evolution. Several more or less

specific types have been suggested, but there is room for dis-
agreement on such particulars, as shown by several recent papers
on the subject.[10, 11] The best that can be said is that extensive
experimental work will be needed before a well-supported hypothesis can be developed. I shall also omit further discussion
of the question what factors may have operated as agents of
natural selection during this process, and for much the same
reasons. Instead, the following remarks are intended to indicate
some of the consequences of the general approach outlined
above.

Given a chemically complex environment as yet devoid of
living organisms, our first problem is to postulate a mechanism
that can account for the appearance of life therein. But the possibility of doing so depends in turn on knowing what we shall
mean by "life." The macrobiologist may not find it particularly
difficult to set up a number of criteria that are unlikely to cause
confusion; his higher plants and animals exhibit several properties which, taken together, permit a comparatively sharp delimi-
tation of living from nonliving systems. But for the microbiologist, who concerns himself with small, smaller, and smallest
living entities, it is not at all easy to produce a satisfactory
definition. Pirie has pointed out the difficulties in the following
passage:

> Now, however, systems are being discovered and studied
> which are neither obviously living nor obviously dead, and it
> is necessary to define these words or else give up using them,
> and coin others. When one is asked whether a filter-passing
> virus is living or dead the only sensible answer is, "I don't
> know; we know a number of things it will do and a number
> of things it won't and if some commission will define the word
> 'living' I will try to see how the virus fits into the definition."
> This answer does not as a rule satisfy the questioner, who gen-
> erally has strong but unfortunate opinions about what he
> means by the words living and dead.[12]

I do not see how one can disagree with this conclusion. And
from this it follows that an operationally more useful approach

than the search for an acceptable definition is needed as a guide to the problem of the origin of life.

This, I believe, is provided by the concept of integrative levels, which implies that with an increase in the complexity of a system new properties may arise which are not predictable from those of the constituent units. To illustrate: molecules, such as those of H_2O, generally display characteristics quite distinct from those of the atoms of which they are composed, and a knowledge of the latter does not suffice to anticipate the former. Of course, this statement can be challenged on the basis of the argument that we should be in a position to do so if we had an adequate understanding of the properties of hydrogen and oxygen atoms. But the objection seems to me invalid because it rests on the premise that such an understanding can be attained by studying the behavior of atoms in isolation. And this is not the case; only by including a knowledge of the properties of compound molecules have the concepts been derived that are needed to make more or less accurate predictions possible. It is clear that our current atomic theory could not have been developed if it had not been for extensive studies on various kinds of molecules; similarly, the existence and properties of the elementary particles of matter have in part been inferred from the known behavior of larger units. In fact, the whole structure of natural science is the result of extrapolations, in two opposite directions.

For the present purpose it is useful to consider a more biological example. It can hardly be doubted that the process we are in the habit of calling thinking can ultimately be referred to a series of special physical and chemical events that take place in the brain. One might thus be led to conclude that it should be possible to predict that a certain number of molecules, of special composition and arranged in a definite pattern, would yield a system that could "think," if the nature of these reactions were known well enough. Nevertheless, the very search for such substances and the study of the requisite organization must start from the knowledge that thinking exists; it seems to me more than doubtful that even the most thorough investigation of the behavior of inanimate matter, however intricate its composition and organizational pattern, would ever suffice to deduce a priori the occurrence of thought processes. Now, the merit of the principle of integrative levels is exactly that it eliminates the need for such specific deductions; it merely implies that we should expect inanimate matter in a state of sufficient complexity to exhibit new properties, as yet unknown and unpredictable, and discoverable only by an empirical approach.

This example brings out another important feature. It shows that, once we are aware of the new property, we can begin to study the relation between the chemical composition and the structural organization of substances involved in its manifestations. And this can be done even if we have not succeeded in formulating a broad enough definition of thought to encompass all its aspects, and therefore to satisfy every student of the process. The concept of integrative levels thus makes it unnecessary to search for a definite starting point, which, even at best, can only be arbitrary. The pertinence of this conclusion to the problem of the origin of life will be obvious. By introducing the idea that *"Life is a special property of matter at a certain stage of complexity,"* we can dispense with a universally acceptable definition of life if it is our primary aim to relate the degree of complexity of a system to the properties it exhibits. The characterization of life as a property of matter also throws fresh light on Haldane's statement:

> But to suppose that one can describe life fully on these lines [that is, in terms of chemical reactions] is to attempt to reduce it to mechanism, which I believe to be impossible. On the other hand, to say that life does not consist of chemical processes is to my mind as futile and untrue as to say that poetry does not consist of words.[13]

The most important aspect of this approach is, however, that it permits the biologist to think about the origin of life as the result of the gradual emergence of entities with special combinations of properties without having to define what these must be in order to justify the conclusion that the complex is "living"; he can limit or extend the minimum requirements to suit his own opinions. It is then not difficult to agree with Pringle's verdict:

> The organism as a coherent machine thus emerges from a diffuse system of chemical reactivity and its properties are added step by step by a process akin to natural selection. Life truly evolves from chaos with no moment of special creation to identify its birth.[14]

On the basis of the generalized concept of evolution outlined above, it seems logical to postulate that, in the course of some thousand millions of years, chemical reactions would have produced an environment of sufficient complexity to cause the spontaneous appearance of systems with the properties of self-duplication, of metabolic activity, and of irritability. To my mind this is as readily conceivable as the proposition that during a similar span of time man has evolved from a primordial living entity, a concept that seems unavoidable in view of the vast amount of geological, paleobiological, biochemical, anatomical, and embryological evidence in its favor.

Acceptance of the postulate that chemical evolution preceded biopoesis further suggests that the organized structures representing primitive life were capable of self-reproduction before they acquired mechanisms by means of which they could chemically transform the components of their environment. As Pirie has pointed out on several occasions, it is entirely possible that many different structures of this sort, potential precursors of more effective systems, may have developed in the complex milieu; but present-day knowledge seems to justify the conclusion that one particular type of complex eventually came to dominance, and served as the starting point for all forms of life with which we are familiar.

Although attractive from an evolutionary point of view, the idea that the first "living organisms" were no more than mere assemblages of physicochemical complexes existing in the environment, and that initially they lacked the property of effecting chemical transformations of the components, implies the need for a rational hypothesis that can account for the development of mechanisms involved in the chemical activities of living organisms. Such a hypothesis is provided by the speculations of Horowitz on the evolution of biochemical syntheses.[15] The argument is based on the one-gene-one-enzyme concept, and on the interpretation of biosynthetic processes as chains of simple step reactions, each one controlled by a special enzyme. In addition, it shows how Haldane's postulate of a primary chemical evolution circumvents a serious difficulty which arises if the problem is approached from a different angle. An example may serve to indicate the line of reasoning.

Let us consider the synthesis of a single, essential amino acid by an organism that can multiply in a medium composed of minerals and sugar. Without entering into details (see Chapter 2), we may represent this process as the net result of n consecutive step reactions, catalyzed by the sequential operation of an equal number of enzymes. It follows that the amino acid cannot be synthesized unless all these enzymes are present; any combination of enzymes short of the full complement is ineffective for the purpose. This entails the further consequence that none of these combinations would confer the slightest selective advantage on the organism, since failure to synthesize the amino acid is equivalent to inability to grow. Now, the biosynthesis of even comparatively simple molecules may require the coöperation of as many as a hundred distinct enzymes; obviously, a correspondingly greater number will be needed for the production of more complicated substances. This very fact seems to preclude the possibility that the enzyme chains operative in biosynthetic reactions can have evolved by a "mutational" sort of mechanism, that is, through the chance occurrence of slight changes. For it must be remembered that the commonly encountered mutations are single-gene mutations, and hence involve only a single enzyme. The above argument would therefore indicate that the genesis of a biosynthetic property by such a mechanism makes it necessary to postulate the summation of a multitude of random events, each one selectively worthless, and thus unlikely to persist.

It is the great merit of Horowitz to have recognized that the paradox ensuing from the above approach is intrinsically the same as the one earlier discussed in connection with the "autotroph hypothesis" of spontaneous generation, and for precisely the same reason. Here, too, the premise has been that a complex system, namely, an elaborate enzyme chain, develops in a simple environment. But, as Horowitz has shown, the difficulty instantly disappears if the relation is reversed, and then a good case can be made out for the thesis that enzyme chains have evolved step by step, and in such a manner that each successive feature is selectively important. This follows from the reasonable assumption that chemical evolution would have yielded, in addition to the preformed constituents from which the first organisms were put together, also the entire series of simpler precursors of these ingredients. As long as the organism can draw upon the complete structures, it can multiply without need for synthetic activity, and during this phase the precursors are not utilized. But when the supply of one of the essential constituents, P_n, has been exhausted, growth by mere accretion must cease. If at this time a "single-gene mutation" has produced a modified organism with the ability to convert the immediate precursor, P_{n-1}, into P_n, the result would be that the variant, possessing an enormous selective advantage over the original type, would become established, and along with it the newly acquired catalyst. The eventual depletion of P_{n-1} would cause the natural selection of a mutant with the capacity to use P_{n-2} for the manufacture of P_{n-1}, and this would thus establish the second catalyst. Proceeding in this manner, a catalytic chain of any desired length can be built up, starting with the "last" member of the series, and each additional biochemical potentiality would be retained because it significantly contributes to the survival value of the organism.

It must by now be evident that the generalized concept of evolution can lead to a rational and fully consistent hypothesis concerning the origin of life and the development of biochemical activities by natural selection of complexes with modified properties. It may not be superfluous, however, to point out that the term "mutational changes" has here been used in a very loose sense, merely to indicate the evolutionary significance of random and infrequent events involving a discrete change in some essential component of a complex system. These events need not be comparable to the typical gene mutations familiar to the "macrobiologist," either in kind or in origin. It must further be understood that so far nothing has been said about the methods whereby the properties of primordial forms of life were transmitted. Although straightforward duplication, followed by fission, could be postulated, other mechanisms may also have played a role. It is, for example, possible that special characteristics possessed by different entities may have combined through the formation of larger complexes; in fact, it is probable that such processes have occurred because it is difficult to imagine that typical cellular organisms could have emerged without assuming that they were gradually assembled from smaller units. It might even be argued that such phenomena can still be observed in present-day organisms, as in the case of transduction. But as long as we are still groping in the dark when trying to formulate in a more precise manner the early stages of biological evolution, it does not seem profitable to dwell on these matters.

There is, however, one particular aspect of the foregoing discussion that calls for a somewhat more detailed treatment; this pertains to the actual demonstration that biochemical gains in the sense of Horowitz occur. In Chapter 5 it has already been mentioned that the evolutionary approach is utterly inconsistent with the notion that all mutations involve losses, and that the failure of past experiments to support the concept of biochemical evolution may, at least in part, be attributed to the special methodology used for the isolation of biochemical mutants. This leads to the question whether the hypothesis, which is logically so attractive, cannot be strengthened by experimental evidence. The following remarks are intended to show in what manner such evidence may be obtained.

We shall first consider a phenomenon that is familiar to many microbiologists. It is sometimes found that a bacterial culture, immediately after its isolation from natural sources, can grow only in media supplemented with vitamins or amino acids, but that, after a number of transfers, it can grow equally well if these supplements are omitted. This behavior suggests that the strain has acquired the ability, initially lacking, to synthesize the growth factors. This might have happened as the result of mutations, and in that case the phenomenon in question would constitute evidence for the occurrence of gain mutants. This is not the only possible interpretation of the observed facts, however, and careful experiments are needed to rule out alternative explanations, especially the possibility that the original isolate might itself have been a loss mutant of a naturally occurring wild type to which it could revert by back mutation.

It is also possible to search for gain mutants more directly. But then it is necessary to isolate the mutants by methods other than those developed for the detection of loss mutants. After treatment of a suspension of microbes with mutagenic agents and plating on a minimal medium, one could, for example, isolate a large number of clones from colonies that develop under these conditions, and examine their biosynthetic abilities in the hope of finding new types with increased powers of synthesis. Such a procedure is obviously very cumbersome, since a large number of isolates would undoubtedly represent unchanged wild-type individuals. One might, therefore, concentrate on the isolation of "morphological" mutants from the minimal medium, not because these are more likely to correspond to biochemical gain mutants, but because they can readily be recognized as variants, and by criteria that are not prejudicial in a biochemical sense.

For such investigations the choice of organism is of paramount importance. It should be evident that a microbe which can grow in a mineral medium with a single organic carbon source would be wholly inappropriate; it would be difficult to look for gains in biosynthetic properties since we do not know in what direction these might manifest themselves. It seems more logical to use an organism with complex nutrient requirements, and to determine whether it can yield mutants able to grow in media deficient in some growth factor required by the parent strain. In that case it may even appear feasible to detect the presence of gain mutants with predetermined properties by plating on media lacking some specific ingredient. In theory, at least, this approach is sound and simple. Nevertheless, it has implications that must be clearly recognized if it is to yield satisfactory results. This statement can best be illustrated by an example.

Suppose we wish to perform such studies with an organism whose nutrient requirements include thiamin, and look for the appearance of thiamin-independent mutants. On a thiamin-free medium only these variants will produce colonies, and hence they can be spotted without difficulty. The experiment is therefore simple to execute. But it should be remembered that genotypically different individuals will almost invariably be the result of single-gene mutations. This implies that thiamin-independent mutants will not arise unless the inability of the parent strain to grow without thiamin were due to the lack of one single gene or enzyme operative in the biosynthesis of the vitamin. In view of the large number of steps involved in the latter, the above prerequisite for a positive outcome of the test will rarely be fulfilled. In a much more drastic manner the argument can be presented in the form of a suggestion for an experiment designed to reveal a mutational change that would cause a colon bacterium, for example, to acquire the ability to photosynthesize. Inoculation of a medium suitable only for the development of photosynthetic organisms with a large number of individuals treated with mutagenic agents should obviously permit the ready detection of photosynthetic mutants. It is hard to believe, however, that anyone would actually contemplate performing this experiment, in spite of its relative simplicity. It is too obvious that an enormous number of changes are necessary to produce a functional photosynthetic apparatus in the test organism, and the concatenation of such events, even during the course of a prolonged study, is so improbable as to discourage the attempt. In principle the same difficulties are inherent in experiments of the kind mentioned earlier, although there they may not be so immediately apparent.

But this critique also indicates how the methodology can be modified in order to make the approach both more promising and more crucial. Any attempt to submit the Horowitz hypothesis to a decisive experimental test must be squarely based on the postulate that it is only the last catalyst of a biosynthetic chain that will appear as a permanent addition to the enzyme complement of the organism under investigation. It is, therefore, not enough to use a medium from which a special growth factor has been eliminated for the detection of gain mutants; instead, the medium should be amply supplied with the immediate precursor of the substance omitted. If one were to find variants that can grow under these conditions, they can be further treated with a view to inducing additional changes, leading to offspring that can use the next to the last precursor, and so on.

Perhaps the best general design for experiments of this kind would combine the principle of natural selection with the approach outlined above. This can be realized through the use of liquid media containing a suboptimal amount of one particular growth factor and, in addition, a large supply of its immediate precursor. The presence of the former would ensure limited growth of the initial strain; the inclusion of the latter would permit continued development of variants that can accomplish the last step of the synthesis. In transfers of the culture to media devoid of the growth factor proper these variants should outgrow the parent type, and repeated subcultures in media of appropriate composition can be resorted to as a means of establishing additional gains. Eventually it might thus become possible to demonstrate the gradual acquisition of synthetic ability. The larger is the number of step reactions covered by such studies, the more meaningful will be the results. This requires, however, a considerable knowledge concerning the details of the biosynthesis of substances such as the vitamins and amino acids, which seem to hold out the most promise for investigations on biochemical evolution. Unfortunately, the available information is as yet insufficient to encourage experimentation along these lines on an extensive scale.

Even in the absence of direct experimental support, the Horowitz hypothesis has much to recommend it as a starting point for some further deductions. If we think of the primitive organisms as initially devoid of biosynthetic activity, gradually acquiring such properties in a manner compatible with general evolutionary precepts, it must be concluded that some time after the self-duplicating units had appeared a process was initiated that can best be described by the term "biochemical evolution." Its logical place in the sequence of evolutionary phases is between the chemical evolution and the more characteristically biological evolution in the sense of Darwin.

As previously mentioned, it seems futile to speculate on the nature of the first living entities. It may suffice to indicate that units with the requisite degree of complexity could have been formed as the result of adsorption or coacervation; both these mechanisms can lead to the genesis of nonhomogeneous aggregates, comprising a smaller or larger number of different components. Ultimately such ill-defined, noncellular complexes must, of course, have given rise to cellular units. Just how far an evolution toward greater structural complexity and organization would have had to progress before biochemical evolution could begin to play a significant role in further developments is a question that must be left unanswered in view of our inadequate knowledge. It is readily conceivable that various metabolic properties may have originated at different levels.

Although these considerations seem to militate against attempts to reconstruct the consecutive stages traversed during the course of biochemical evolution, it is, nevertheless, possible to indicate the general trend; this can be inferred in part from theoretical arguments, and in part from the biochemical properties exhibited by extant microorganisms. The result seems to me of sufficient interest to justify the inclusion of a brief outline of the approach.

It is probable that aerobic metabolism did not evolve until green-plant photosynthesis had created an environment in which oxygen was available. The first biochemical patterns would thus be representative of the diverse types of anaerobic processes. In line with our primary assumption, we must grant that entities with the most complex nutrient requirements, that is, with the least developed biosynthetic activity and the greatest dependence on a complex environment, antedated those with more restricted needs. The first phase of biochemical evolution would therefore have involved the gradual acquisition of the ability to use progressively less complex mixtures of organic ingredients for the production of the chemical constituents of the organisms. This phase can thus be characterized as an evolution toward increased independence on a medium replete with a multitude of organic materials. The theoretical limit of such independence is reached with the appearance of organisms that no longer require any organic substances. These are the chemo- and photoautotrophic organisms. Among the anaerobic microbes known at present this property is exhibited by the causative agents of sulfate reduction and of the methane fermentation, by the green and purple sulfur bacteria, and by the algae. Far from being "primitive," the metabolic characteristics of such organisms now appear to occupy a position near the end of the scale of biochemical evolution.

During this phase the typical pattern of oxidative metabolism could have originated; and the metabolic properties of some present-day anaerobes provide support for this contention. The most striking illustration is the fact that the obligatorily anaerobic bacteria responsible for sulfate reduction and methane production can oxidize a variety of substrates to completion, with sulfate and carbon dioxide, respectively, as the ultimate hydrogen or electron acceptors. Another point worth mentioning is that the sulfate-reducing bacteria possess cytochromes (Chapter 2), the most characteristic components of the catalytic system operative in aerobic metabolism; the methane-producing bacteria have not yet been investigated in this respect. In other anaerobes, such as the lactic acid bacteria, whose metabolism is not oxidative, and which require a large number of different growth factors, cytochromes are never found.

The conclusion that chemo- and photoautotrophy represent the final stages of biochemical evolution leads to the problem of the order of appearance of these processes. There are, I believe, sound reasons in favor of the thesis that anaerobic chemoautotrophy preceded photoautotrophy, the latter also starting from an anaerobic pattern. In both these metabolic types carbon dioxide can serve as the only carbon source for the synthesis of all the cellular constituents, which indicates a fundamental similarity in the enzymatic equipment required for the conversion of carbon dioxide into cell material. The difference in these processes is, however, that photosynthesis displays an additional property, namely, that of utilizing radiant energy for the photochemical production of reducing substances from water; hence the photosynthetic organisms can reduce carbon dioxide at the expense of these reducing agents, that is, ultimately of water. While the chemoautotrophs are no longer dependent on a supply of organic substances, the photoautotrophs have thus acquired a new metabolic feature, which in the end makes them independent even of oxidizable inorganic matter, still needed by the chemoautotrophs for the assimilation of carbon dioxide. But the photosynthetic bacteria, too, require oxidizable inorganic substances, such as hydrogen sulfide or molecular hydrogen. Metabolically they are therefore intermediate between the chemoautotrophs and the green plants. From the point of view of the utilization of the oxidizable material, the photosynthetic bacteria are, however, considerably more efficient than corresponding chemoautotrophs;

this follows from the fact that the former do not derive the energy for biosynthetic reactions exclusively from the oxidation of the substrate, but in large part from absorbed radiant energy. They are, therefore, on their way toward independence of reducing compounds; but complete independence is achieved only with the development of the mechanism operative in green-plant photosynthesis. Here, the oxidation of water, with the concomitant evolution of oxygen, is the ultimate source of reducing capacity.

This outline of the main stages of biochemical evolution, although based on the metabolic patterns of present-day bacteria, should not be taken to mean that these patterns can be used as an infallible guide for tracing the phylogeny of these organisms. In the first place, the now known metabolic types may have developed originally in organisms quite unlike bacteria, and have been perpetuated through entirely unknown transformations. This argument remains valid even though it should be admitted that the complicated enzymatic system needed for a chemo- or photoautotrophic mode of life would seem to call for a level of organization that could hardly have been accommodated in units of much smaller size. In the second place, it would be rash to deny the possibility that extant bacterial types with requirements for an organic substrate and a variety of special growth factors might represent descendants of less exacting organisms which had suffered a loss of synthetic ability, as postulated on good grounds by Twort and Ingraham, and by Lwoff (see Chapter 5).

On the other hand, this admonition does not detract from the main thesis, that biochemical evolution can be characterized as a process whereby living organisms became increasingly more independent, first of organic matter, and subsequently also of inorganic reducing substances. When this final stage had been reached, a continuous supply of organic compounds was ensured, with no other external energy source besides solar radiation. From here on the grand experiment of evolution could proceed in new directions. The combination of individual cellular units into larger complexes resulted in the appearance of the multicellular organisms, permitting a differentiation beyond the cellular level. Concurrently, novel potentialities could arise, through which a new degree of control over the environment became possible, even at the expense of biosynthetic activity.

It seems to me that the generalized concept of evolution, as comprising physical, chemical, biochemical, and biological phases, together with the principle of integrative levels, provide a rational basis for thinking about life in all its aspects. This approach also implies a satisfactory solution to Samuel Butler's enigma. For we *can* "assume life of some kind omnipresent forever throughout matter," since "life" is regarded as a property of matter at a particular state of complexity. At the same time we can also "assume an act of spontaneous generation," since this is the equivalent of assuming the attainment, "somewhere and somewhen," of the requisite degree of complexity. Thus there seems to be no reason for asserting that we "cannot have it both ways." In essence, the outlook here presented yields a continuum from matter to life, wherein a discontinuity arises mainly as the result of the human need for categorization to which we are compelled by the use of words.

Thus we are left with the final problem of formulating a "scientific Athanasian Creed." If we contemplate the transition from elementary particles to atoms; from atoms to molecules; from molecules to complexes; from "dead" organic matter to living organisms; from microbes to man, the most complicated organism known to us today, with powers even to destroy himself and the civilizations he has built up over a period of thousands of years; then the inevitable question arises: from man to . . . what?

Here I would end with a quotation from André Gide's *Journals:*

> If I had to formulate a credo, I should say: God is not behind us. He is to come. He must be sought, not at the beginning, but at the end of the evolution. He is terminal and not initial. He is the supreme and final point toward which all nature tends in time.[16]

This, I believe, comes close to a scientific Athanasian Creed.

REFERENCES

CHAPTER 1

1. O. Rahn, *Microbes of merit* (Jaques Cattell Press, Lancaster, Pa., 1945).

2. *Oeuvres de Pasteur,* réunies par Pasteur Vallery-Radot (Masson, Paris, 1922), Vol. 2 (1863), p. 165.

3. F. Cohn, *Uber Bakterien, die kleinsten lebenden Wesen* (Carl Habel, Berlin, 1872).

4. S. Winogradsky, *Microbiologie du sol; Oeuvres complètes* (Masson, Paris, 1949).

5. M. W. Beijerinck, *Verzamelde Geschriften* (Delft, 1921–1940), Vol. 1–6.

6. H. L. Jensen and H. I. Petersen, *Acta Agric. Scand. 2,* 215 (1952).

7. A. Kistner, *Proc. Koninkl. Ned. Akad. Wetenschap.* [C] *56,* 443 (1953).

8. L. E. den Dooren de Jong, "Bijdrage tot de kennis van het mineralisatieproces" (thesis, Delft, 1926).

9. N. L. Söhngen, "Het ontstaan en verdwijnen van waterstof en methaan onder den invloed van het organische leven" (thesis, Delft, 1906).

10. S. L. Neave and A. M. Buswell, *J. Am. Chem. Soc. 52,* 3308 (1930); G. E. Symons and A. M. Buswell, *J. Am. Chem. Soc. 55,* 2028 (1933); D. Tarvin and A. M. Buswell, *J. Am. Chem. Soc. 56,* 1751 (1934).

11. C. G. T. P. Schnellen, "Onderzoekingen over de methaangisting" (thesis, Delft, 1947).

12. K. T. Wieringa, *Antonie van Leeuwenhoek. J. Microbiol. Serol. 3,* 263 (1936); *6,* 251 (1940).

13. H. A. Barker, *Arch. Mikrobiol. 8,* 415 (1937); H. A. Barker and S. M. Taha, *J. Bacteriol. 43,* 347 (1942).

14. H. A. Barker and M. D. Kamen, *Proc. Nat. Acad. Sci. U.S. 26,* 477 (1945).

15. A. J. Kluyver and W. Verhoeven, *Antonie van Leeuwenhoek. J. Microbiol. Serol. 20,* 241 (1954).

16. J. K. Baars, "Over sulfaatreductie door bacteriën" (thesis, Delft, 1930).

17. H. A. Barker, *Arch. Mikrobiol. 7,* 404 (1936).

18. A. M. Buswell and S. W. Sollo, *J. Am. Chem. Soc. 70,* 1778 (1948).

19. T. C. Stadtman and H. A. Barker, *Arch. Biochem.* 21, 256 (1949).

20. F. Lipmann, *Advances in Enzymol.* 1, 99, (1941); in D. E. Green, ed., *Currents in biochemical research* (Interscience, New York, 1946).

CHAPTER 2

1. H. D. Slade and C. H. Werkman, *Arch. Biochem.* 2, 97 (1943).

2. H. G. Wood, R. W. Brown, and C. H. Werkman, *Arch. Biochem.* 6, 243 (1945).

3. R. Schoenheimer, *The dynamic state of body constituents* (Harvard University Press, Cambridge, 1942). See also M. D. Kamen, *Radioactive tracers in biology* (Academic Press, New York, ed. 2, 1951).

4. D. Hogness, M. Cohn, and J. Monod, *Biochim. et Biophys. Acta* 16, 99 (1955).

5. M. V. Simpson and S. F. Velick, *J. Biol. Chem.* 208, 61 (1954).

6. I. C. Gunsalus and M. Gibbs, *J. Biol. Chem.* 194, 871 (1952).

7. M. Gibbs and R. D. DeMoss, *J. Biol. Chem.* 207, 689 (1954).

8. H. Gest and J. O. Lampen, *J. Biol. Chem.* 194, 555 (1952).

9. B. L. Horecker, *J. Cellular Comp. Physiol.* 41, Suppl. 1, 137 (1953); *Brewers Dig.* 28, 214 (1953); E. Racker, *Advances in Enzymol.* 15, 141 (1954); S. S. Cohen in D. M. Greenberg, ed., *Chemical pathways of metabolism* (Academic Press, New York, 1954).

10. I. C. Gunsalus in W. D. McElroy and B. Glass, eds., *The mechanism of enzyme action* (Johns Hopkins Press, Baltimore, 1954).

11. F. Lipmann, *Bacteriol. Revs.* 17, 1 (1953); *Science* 120, 855 (1954).

12. D. J. O'Kane, *J. Bacteriol.* 43, 7 (1942).

13. J. R. Postgate, *Biochem. J.* (*London*) 56, XI (1954); 58, IX (1954).

14. M. F. Utter, F. Lipmann, and C. H. Werkman, *J. Biol. Chem.* 154, 723 (1944); 158, 521 (1945).

15. F. Lynen, *Federation Proc.* 12, 683 (1953); *Biochim. et Biophys. Acta,* 12, 299 (1953).

16. P. H. Abelson, E. Bolton, R. Britten, D. B. Cowie, and R. B. Roberts, *Proc. Nat. Acad. Sci. U.S.* 39, 1020 (1953).

17. V. du Vigneaud, *A trail of research in sulfur chemistry and metabolism and related fields* (Cornell University Press, Ithaca, 1952).

18. H. A. Barker, *J. Cellular Comp. Physiol.* 8, 231 (1936).

19. G. Giesberger, "Beiträge zur Kenntnis der Gattung *Spirillum* Ehbg (thesis, Utrecht, 1936).

20. C. E. Clifton, *Enzymologia* 4, 246 (1937); *Advances in Enzymol.* 6, 269 (1946); see also C. E. Clifton in C. H. Werkman and

P. W. Wilson, eds., *Bacterial physiology* (Academic Press, New York, 1951).

21. F. H. Westheimer, H. F. Fisher, E. E. Conn, and B. Vennesland, *J. Am. Chem. Soc. 73,* 2403 (1951); *J. Biol. Chem. 202,* 687 (1953).

22. T. A. Geissman, *Quart. Rev. Biol. 24,* 309 (1949).

23. E. Work and D. L. Dewey, *J. Gen. Microbiol. 9,* 394 (1953).

CHAPTER 3

1. E. I. Rabinowitch, *Photosynthesis and related processes* (Interscience, New York), vol. I (1945); vol. II, pt. 1 (1951).

2. C. B. van Niel, "Biochemical problems of the chemo-autotrophic bacteria," *Physiol. Revs. 23,* 338 (1943).

3. A. F. Lebedeff, "Ueber die Assimilation des Kohlenstoffes bei wasserstoffoxydierenden Bakterien," *Biochem. Z. 7,* 1 (1908).

4. C. B. van Niel, "The comparative biochemistry of photosynthesis," in J. Franck and W. E. Loomis, eds., *Photosynthesis in plants* (Iowa State College Press, Ames, 1949), pp. 437–495.

5. L. S. Levitt, "Photosynthesis as a photoelectric phenomenon," *Science 118,* 696 (1953); "The role of magnesium in photosynthesis," *Science 120,* 33 (1954).

6. M. Calvin, "The path of carbon in photosynthesis," *Chem. Eng. News 31,* 1622 (1953).

7. C. B. van Niel, M. B. Allen, and B. E. Wright, "On the photochemical reduction of nitrate by algae," *Biochim. et Biophys. Acta 12,* 67 (1953).

8. W. Vishniac and S. Ochoa, "Fixation of carbon dioxide coupled to photochemical reduction of pyridine nucleotides by chloroplast preparations," *J. Biol. Chem. 195,* 75 (1952).

9. D. I. Arnon, M. B. Allen, and F. R. Whatley, "Photosynthesis by isolated chloroplasts," *Nature 174,* 394 (1954).

10. E. C. Wassink, E. Katz, and R. Dorrestein, "On photosynthesis and fluorescence of bacteriochlorophyll in Thiorhodaceae," *Enzymologia 10,* 285 (1942).

11. H. Larsen, C. Yocum, and C. B. van Niel, "On the energetics of the photosyntheses in green sulfur bacteria," *J. Gen. Physiol. 36,* 161 (1952).

12. C. B. van Niel, "Bacterial photosyntheses," in J. B. Sumner and K. Myrbäck, eds., *The enzymes* (Academic Press, New York, 1952), Vol. II, Pt. 2, pp. 1074–1088 (1952).

13. H. E. Davenport and R. Hill, "The preparation and some properties of cytochrome *f*," *Proc. Roy. Soc.* (London) [B] *139,* 327, (1952).

14. S. R. Elsden, "The utilization of organic compounds by photosynthetic bacteria," in the Fourth Symposium of the Society for Gen-

eral Microbiology, *Autotrophic micro-organisms* (Cambridge University Press, Cambridge, 1954), pp. 202–223.

15. L. N. M. Duysens, "Reversible photo-oxidation of a cytochrome pigment in photosynthesizing *Rhodospirillum rubrum*," *Nature, 173,* 692 (1954).

16. L. R. Blinks, "The role of accessory pigments in photosynthesis," in the Fourth Symposium of the Society for General Microbiology, *Autotrophic micro-organisms* (Cambridge University Press, Cambridge, 1954), pp. 224–246

17. W. Arnold and J. R. Oppenheimer, "Internal conversion in the photosynthetic mechanism of blue-green algae," *J. Gen. Physiol. 33,* 423 (1950).

18. L. N. M. Duysens, "Transfer of excitation energy in photosynthesis" (thesis, Utrecht, 1952).

19. E. Racker, "Synthesis of carbohydrates from carbon dioxide and hydrogen in a cell-free system," *Nature 175,* 249 (1955).

CHAPTER 4

1. H. Karström, "Ueber die Enzymbildung in Bakterien" (thesis, Helsinki, 1930).

2. L. H. C. Perquin, "Bijdrage tot de kennis der oxydatieve dissimilatie van *Aspergillus niger* van Tieghem" (thesis, Delft, 1938).

3. A. J. Kluyver and L. H. C. Perquin, *Biochem. Z. 266,* 68 (1933).

4. E. van Olden, *Proc. Koninkl. Ned. Akad. Wetenschap., 43,* 635 (1940).

5. W. Verhoeven, A. L. Koster, and M. C. A. van Nievelt, *Antonie van Leeuwenhoek. J. Microbiol. Serol. 20,* 273 (1954); A. J. Kluyver and W. Verhoeven, *Antonie van Leeuwenhoek. J. Microbiol. Serol. 20,* 337 (1954).

6. E. F. Gale and R. Davies, ed., *Adaptation in micro-organisms* (Cambridge University Press, Cambridge, 1953). This is a symposium organized by the Society for General Microbiology. Among the contributors were Stanier, Hinshelwood, Spiegelman, Monod, and Pollock.

7. S. Jackson and C. N. Hinshelwood, *Proc. Roy. Soc. (London) B 136,* 562 (1949); C. N. Hinshelwood and S. Jackson, *Proc. Roy. Soc. (London) B 137,* 88 (1950); A. C. Baskett and C. N. Hinshelwood, *Proc. Roy. Soc. (London) B 139,* 58 (1951).

8. F. J. Ryan, *J. Gen. Microbiol. 7,* 69 (1952).

9. A. C. R. Dean and C. N. Hinshelwood, *Proc. Roy. Soc. (London) B 142,* 45, 225, 471 (1954).

10. R. Y. Stanier, *J. Bacteriol. 54,* 339 (1947); *Ann. Rev. Microbiol. 5,* 35 (1951).

11. R. Repaske and P. W. Wilson, *Proc. Nat. Acad. Sci. U.S. 139,* 225 (1953).

12. J. Monod and M. Cohn, *Advances in Enzymol. 13*, 67 (1952); J. Monod, *Schweiz. Z. allgem. Pathol. u. Bakteriol. 15*, 407 (1952).

13. S. Benzer, *Biochim. et Biophys. Acta 11*, 383 (1953).

14. F. Bernheim and W. E. DeTurk, *J. Bacteriol. 65*, 65 (1953).

15. G. Cohen-Bazire and M. Jolit, *Ann. inst. Pasteur 84*, 937 (1953).

16. M. R. Pollock, *Brit. J. Exptl. Pathol. 31*, 739 (1950); *33*, 587 (1952); M. R. Pollock and C. J. Perret, *Brit. J. Exptl. Pathol. 32*, 387 (1951).

17. E. E. D. Manson, M. R. Pollock, and E. J. Tridgell, *J. Gen. Microbiol. 11*, 493 (1954).

18. J. L. Koppel, C. J. Porter, and B. F. Crocker, *J. Gen. Physiol. 36*, 703 (1953); C. J. Porter, R. Holmes, and B. F. Crocker, *J. Gen. Physiol. 37*, 271 (1953).

19. M. R. Pollock and A. M. Torriani, *Compt. rend. 237*, 276 (1953).

20. H. O. Halvorson and S. Spiegelman, *J. Bacteriol. 64*, 207 (1952); *65*, 496, 601 (1953).

21. B. Rotman and S. Spiegelman, *J. Bacteriol. 68*, 419 (1954).

22. D. Hogness, M. Cohn, and J. Monod, *Biochim. et Biophys. Acta 16*, 99 (1955).

23. E. F. Gale and J. P. Folkes, *Nature 173*, 1223 (1954).

24. J. Monod, *Growth Symposium 11* 223 (1947); S. Spiegelman, *Symposia. Soc. Exptl. Biol. 2*, 86 (1948).

CHAPTER 5

1. M. W. Beijerinck, "Mutation bei Mikroben," *Folia Mikrobiologica 1*, 1 (1912); *Verzamelde Geschriften*, vol. 5 (1921), pp. 25–89.

2. I. M. Lewis, "Bacterial variation with special reference to some mutabile strains of colon bacteria in synthetic media," *J. Bacteriol. 28*, 619 (1934).

3. J. Lederberg, E. M. Lederberg, N. D. Zinder, and E. R. Lively, "Recombination analysis of bacterial heredity," *Cold Spring Harbor Symposia Quant. Biol. 16*, 413 (1951).

4. J. Lederberg, L. L. Cavalli, and E. Lederberg, "Sex compatability in Escherichia coli," *Genetics 37*, 720 (1952).

5. W. Hayes, "Recombination in *Bact. coli* K 12," *Nature 169*, 118, 1017 (1952).

6. B. Ephrussi, *Nucleo-cytoplasmic relations in microorganisms* (Clarendon Press, Oxford, 1953).

7. G. W. Beadle, "Biochemical genetics," *Chem. Revs. 37*, 15 (1945).

8. A. Lwoff, "Etude sur les fonctions perdues," *Ann. fermentations 2*, 419 (1936); *L'Evolution physiologique* (Hermann, Paris, 1943).

9. W. Braun, "Bacterial dissociation; a critical review of a phenomenon of bacterial variation," *Bacteriol. Revs. 11,* 75 (1947); *Bacterial genetics* (Saunders, Philadelphia and London, 1953).

CHAPTER 6

1. Samuel Butler, *The notebooks of Samuel Butler,* Selected, arranged, and edited by H. F. Jones (Dutton, New York, 1917), p. 323.
2. R. Dubos, *Louis Pasteur* (Little, Brown, Boston, 1950), pp. 395–397.
3. J. B. S. Haldane, "The origin of life," *Rationalist Annual, 1929;* reprinted in *The inequality of man* (London, 1932).
4. G. Hardin, "Darwin and the heterotroph hypothesis," *Sci. Monthly 70,* 178 (1950).
5. A. I. Oparin, *The origin of life,* trans. S. Morgulis (Macmillan, New York, 1938).
6. S. L. Miller, "A production of amino acids under possible primitive earth conditions," *Science 117,* 528 (1953).
7. M. Calvin, "Chemical evolution and the origin of life," University of California Radiation Laboratory Report, 2124 (1953).
8. J. D. Bernal, *The physical basis of life* (Routledge and Kegan Paul, London, 1951).
9. V. M. Goldschmidt, "Geochemical aspects of the origin of complex organic molecules on the earth, as precursors to organic life," *New Biology 12,* 97 (1952).
10. H. C. Urey, "On the early chemical history of the earth and the origin of life," *Proc. Nat. Acad. Sci. U. S. 38,* 351 (1952).
11. J. B. S. Haldane, "The origins of life," *New Biology 16,* 12 (1954); J. D. Bernal, "The origin of life," *New Biology 16,* 28 (1954); N. W. Pirie, "On making and recognizing life," *New Biology 16,* 41 (1954); J. W. S. Pringle, "The evolution of living matter," *New Biology 16,* 54 (1954).
12. N. W. Pirie, "The meaninglessness of the terms life and living," in J. Needham and D. Green, eds., *Perspectives of biochemistry* (Cambridge University Press, Cambridge, 1937), p. 12.
13. J. B. S. Haldane, *What is life?* (Boni & Gaer, New York, 1947), p. 56.
14. Pringle, reference 11, p. 66.
15. N. H. Horowitz, "On the evolution of biochemical syntheses," *Proc. Nat. Acad. Sci. U. S. 31,* 153 (1945).
16. André Gide, *The journals of André Gide,* trans. J. O'Brien (Knopf, New York, 1948), vol. 2, p. 122.